The Guide to Station

*Frontispiece: Blast furnace blowing engine at the
Ironbridge Gorge Museum, Shropshire.*

The Guide to
STATIONARY
STEAM ENGINES

Geoffrey Hayes

MPC

British Library Cataloguing in Publication Data
Hayes, G. (Geoffrey), *1932-*
   A Guide to Stationary Steam Engines. — 2nd ed
   1. Great Britain. Industrial antiquities:
   Stationary steam engines — visitor's guides
I. Title
621.160941

ISBN 0 86190 354 4

First published 1981
Revised second edition 1990
© G. Hayes 1990

Cover illustration: Trencherfield Mill, Wigan
(photo: G. Hayes)

Published by Moorland Publishing Co Ltd,
Moor Farm Road West, Ashbourne,
Derbyshire, England DE6 1HD

Printed in Great Britain by
Dotesios Printers Ltd, Trowbridge, Wiltshire

CONTENTS

Acknowledgements   6

Introduction to Second Edition   6

Introduction   7

Glossary and Abbreviations   13

1   On Site Preservation —
  Public Access on a Regular Basis   15

2   Engines in Museums (Public and Private) —
  Or on Public Display   50

3   On Site Preservation —
  Access on Open Days   95

4   On Site Preservation —
  Access by Arrangement Only   107

Appendix   150

Index   158

INTRODUCTION TO SECOND EDITION

Since the publication of the first edition of this book a number of changes have occurred in the field of steam engine preservation. A number of additional engines have been preserved and made available for public inspection, while new museums have opened, but sadly some engines have since been scrapped or public access has now been denied.

On the positive side has been the opening of the Greater Manchester Museum of Science & Industry at the Liverpool Road Station, Manchester — a vast new museum to delight anyone interested in steam power and early engineering. Other new museums include the Kidwelly Tinplate Works Museum in South Wales, the Scottish Mining Museum in Midlothian, Tower Bridge in London, Leeds Industrial Museums and Sheffield Industrial Museum, while there are a number of local museums which now have examples of stationary steam engines on display. Another important addition has been the building of a working replica of Thomas Newcomen's engine of 1712 at The Black Country Museum, Dudley, very close to the site of the original which was the world's first practical steam engine.

One of the saddest changes has been the demolition of the Dee Mill near Oldham in Lancashire, where the engine was kept in immaculate condition by the Northern Mill Engine Society. Now, although the engine still survives, public access is no longer possible. This has been compensated by the full-time opening of the Trencherfield Mill engine at Wigan, which is operated by steam several days a week. Another major loss has been the scrapping of the Fleam Dyke pumping engine.

In order to keep the format of the first edition, an up-to-date appendix has been included in this book with details of new entries, engines where public access is now possible or where an engine has moved from its original site to a museum or other location.

To find the current situation on any museum site, or engine the reader should initially refer to the index. If there is a reference to the appendix (i.e. a bold entry for page 150 onwards), then this should be consulted *before* the main text. Where the engine has been scrapped, or where access is now restricted the original entry has been kept, as the information will be of value as a historical record.

This book presents a unique record of preserved stationary steam engines and will prove as useful and popular as the first edition to the increasing numbers of people who are fascinated by these masterpieces of early engineering.

ACKNOWLEDGEMENTS

Many people have helped in the preparation of this book and thanks are due especially to James Wood (Royal Scottish Museum); Dr E. S. Owen-Jones (Welsh Industrial & Maritime Museum); Mr P. Robinson (Birmingham Science Museum); Dr Francis, Mr P. J. Young, Kenneth Brown, Colin Bowden, Jonathan Minns, Bruce Henderson, John K. Williams, and the owners, engineers and keepers of every engine mentioned.

The author would like to acknowledge the permission of Lancashire County Council (Higher Mill Museum, Helmshore), Welsh Industrial and Maritime Museum, Leicestershire Museum of Technology and the Royal Scottish Museum to reproduce photographs of engines in their keeping; also to Birmingham Museum of Science & Industry, the Science Museum, London and the National Railway Museum for permission to reproduce photographs supplied by them.

INTRODUCTION

The steam engine has its origins in one man, Thomas Newcomen of Dartmouth, Devon. His first commercially applied engine was set to work at a coal mine near Dudley Castle, South Staffordshire, in 1712. How many years of endeavour had gone into its development is not known but it was at least twelve and was probably more. The engine was revolutionary in that it brought together known scientific principles to produce a working machine in a manner never achieved before. That all this had been done by a practical craftsman was the cause of much denigration by the scientific gentry of the day and Newcomen never received the acclaim which was due. However as a devout Baptist it is unlikely that he sought fame and the accomplishment itself he probably regarded as reward enough.

Beam Engines
The basic form of engine that Newcomen devised, with a cylinder connected to one end of a rocking beam and the pump or pumps to the other, continued to be made for some 200 years. Due mainly to the influence of James Watt the beam engine was adapted to provide rotative motion towards the end of the eighteenth century.

In non-rotative form the beam engine attained its zenith in the Cornish pumping engine, which was developed as the name implies by Cornish engineers to drain the metalliferous mines in the Duchy with maximum efficiency. Important steps in its development were the attempts at compounding by Jonathan Hornblower, Arthur Woolf and James Sims. Woolf was the most successful but at the time expansive use of steam in a single-cylinder was found to be most suitable. Cut-off was usually $\frac{1}{4}$ to $\frac{1}{3}$ stroke but as low as $\frac{1}{10}$ was tried. This increased the danger of major breakages due to high initial loadings and in due course some efficiency was sacrificed for reliability. A major feature of the success and economy of the Cornish engine was the method of control by cataract. This governed the *interval* between successive strokes and each stroke was made at full speed, full steam pressure and maximum expansion.
• The economy of the Cornish engine led to its use in the growing public water supply industry but here the rotative engine also became widely adopted. A large number of these rotative engines were built as Woolf compounds, a revival after a spell in the doldrums. The rotative beam engine was put to every

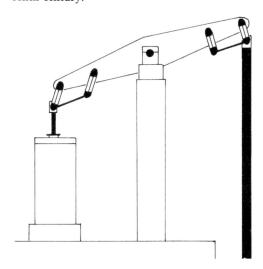

Cornish pumping engine

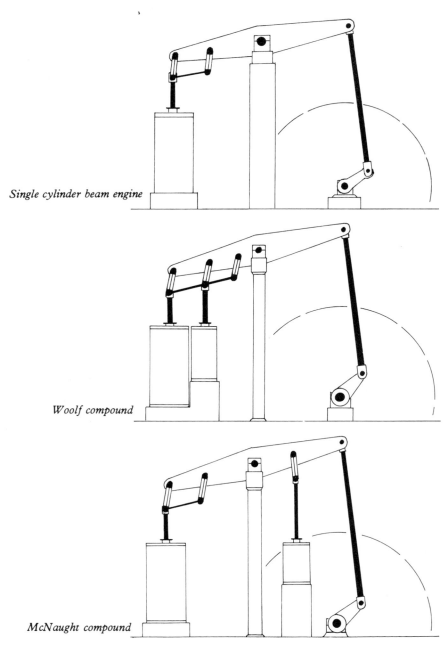

Single cylinder beam engine

Woolf compound

McNaught compound

conceivable use where power was required. It was highly developed as a textile mill engine, the largest being triple expansion. Old single cylinder engines were often converted to compound by a variety of means to give greater power and economy by taking advantage of higher steam pressures.

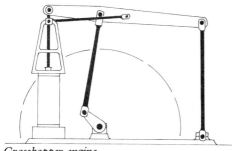

Grasshopper engine

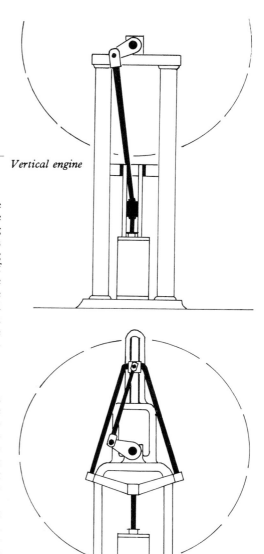

Vertical engine

Steeple engine

Grasshopper Engines

A variant of the beam engine in which the beam has its fulcrum at one end, with the support under the pivot being a rocking column. The other extremity of the beam is coupled to the piston rod and the connecting rod is positioned part way along the length of the beam. This type of engine offered a more compact layout than the conventional engine and achieved quite a wide popularity in small powers. Large engines in this configuration were not common, at least in the UK. There was the inherent disadvantage of the comparatively large mass of column in motion.

Vertical Engines

The beam engine is a bulky machine and in large sizes requires the engine house walls to be an integral part of its structure. The corresponding cost and size was attracting the attention of inventors before the end of the eighteenth century. The Rev Edward Cartwright devised an engine with two contra-rotating crankshafts above the cylinder turned by connecting rods directly coupled to the piston rod. It is unlikely that such an engine was ever built for commercial use but Phineas Crowther in 1802 had success with a similar engine, although with the now conventional single connecting rod and crank. As it was developed in Durham it naturally saw great use as a colliery winding engine and was built to large sizes for this purpose. The traditional Durham winder was single cylinder, but twin cylinder engines were also built in considerable number, and both types were used in nearly all coalfields.

Mill engines were also built in this form in a variety of sizes and small engines used A-frames or one or more cast iron columns to support the crankshaft bearings. In large engines, however, it was necessary to use the engine house walls to give some structural support to the engine.

Variants of the vertical engine were the steeple and table engines, the names giving some idea of their appearance. In these designs the use of return connecting rods enabled the

9

crankshaft to be placed in a lower position than the true vertical engine but neither type was built to any size in the UK.

Horizontal Engines

The major feature of the horizontal engine is that it requires no structure except a substantial bed, and the house can be as light as practicable, or even non-existent! The horizontal engine was made in a tremendous range of sizes and adopted for all conceivable uses. The needs of the Lancashire textile industry produced the most impressive engines in terms of size and efficiency, while the steel trade produced the most powerful for driving rolling mills. The public water supply undertakings used some fine engines for pumping and as running costs were very important they were designed to give economy combined with reliability.

Collieries adopted the horizontal engine virtually as a standard for winding, and apart from some early single cylinder engines these were nearly always twin cylinder using high pressure steam in both cylinders. Some large engines were built having the cross-compound

layout, and twin tandem compound engines were also used to a limited extent. Collieries were also intensive users of engines for air

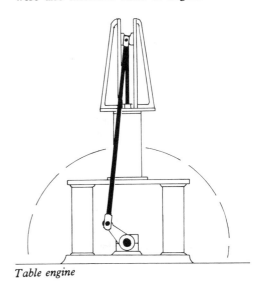

Table engine

Horizontal single cylinder

Horizontal tandem compound

Horizontal cross compound (plan)

10

compressing and driving ventilating fans, and the favoured layout for these was horizontal cross-compound.

Inverted Vertical Engines

This type of engine is the precise opposite of the old vertical, having the crankshaft at floor level with the cylinders at high level supported by columns from the bedplate. Like the horizontal it is 'free-standing'. Initial development was as a marine engine where a compact and powerful engine was needed for the new screw steamships. This feature lent itself to land applications and like the older horizontal design the inverted vertical was used for every purpose in an enormous range of sizes. It made little impact for colliery winding but for the arduous duties of blast furnace blowing and rolling mill drives it was highly developed. One of the latter of 12,000 hp is preserved but not not yet on display.

The textile trade developed the design tremendously and large engines were built for the Lancashire cotton spinning mills. Triple expansion 'marine type' engines with the flywheel at one end of the crankshaft were extensively used, as was also the cross-compound design with the flywheel between the cylinder centre lines. In general the inverted engines ran at higher revolutions than other types, but conversely it was successfully used as a slow speed pumping engine for public water supply. Ecconomy of operation was very important and some fine and very large engines were made for this duty.

The development of electrical power in the latter part of the nineteenth century gave a need for high revolutions in driving the generators. This requirement was met by enclosing the inverted vertical design and running the moving parts in an oil bath. Single acting engines were used at first to avoid reversal of stresses at each stroke but with the introduction of forced lubrication from the 1890s double acting engines were quickly adopted. This type of engine forms the largest group in commercial use today. Its main application was in electrical power generation but other important uses were driving air compressors, fans and centrifugal pumps. Often the engines were non-condensing with the exhaust steam being used for processes or heating services requiring low pressure steam.

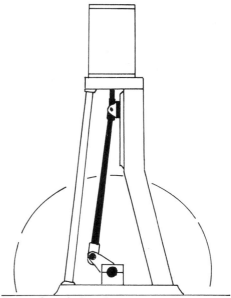

Inverted vertical engine

Non-Rotative Pumping Engines

Edward Bull, a foreman engine erector for Boulton & Watt in the 1790s built several engines in which the cylinder was inverted over the mine shaft and the piston rod coupled directly to the pump rods. He used a 'separate condenser' and was successfully prosecuted by Boulton & Watt for infringement of their patent. However in later years the Bull engine saw considerable use at collieries.

From the mid-nineteenth century onwards a number of designs appeared for direct acting pumps both for mine pumping and as self contained units. A highly successful design for mine pumping was the Davey differential engine whose valve gear was controlled by a separate engine (the 'steam man') which prevented runaway in the event of sudden loss of load. This was always a grave danger with the Cornish engine.

Henry Worthington of New York, whose forebears are said to have hurriedly departed from England after finding themselves on the wrong side at the battle of Naseby, invented the 'Duplex' direct acting pump. With piston rods coupled directly to the pump rams and valve gear on one side driven by the engine on the other it was an ingenious and compact unit. Large engines were built as triple expansion or compound with cylinders in tandem on each side. Small engines had a single cylinder each side. The 'Duplex' pump has probably pumped every known liquid so widely has it been used. Horizontal cylinders were usual.

Finally there is the 'Simplex' pump made so famous by Weir of Cathcart that similar pumps of other makes are often called 'Weir' also. Made in inverted vertical or horizontal form with a single cylinder an ingenious servo-valve gear driven from the piston rod is used. Each maker had his own design but they all used the same basic principles.

Glossary and Abbreviations

Air Pump A pump, usually driven by the engine which removes condensed steam (condensate) and accumulated air from the condenser.

Angle Bob An 'L'-shaped beam pivoted at the corner. Transfers reciprocating motion from horizontal to vertical.

Back Pressure Engine An engine which exhausts into a low pressure steam system.

Bucket Pump Also known as a lift pump because the column of delivered water is on top of the pump piston or 'bucket' and is actually lifted by upward movement of the pump piston.

Centrifugal Pump A form of pump comprising a number of curved vanes mounted on a shaft which rotate within a specially shaped casing. Water enters the casing along the axis of the shaft and is flung out by the vanes to the periphery and thence to the delivery pipe.

Check Valve A valve which allows water (or other fluid) to flow through in one direction, but closes automatically should the flow try to reverse. Other names are clack valve and non-return valve.

Clack Box The housing for a check or clack valve.

Compound Engine An engine with two cylinders (usually) one larger than the other. Steam is admitted to the smaller or high pressure (HP) cylinder then exhausts to the larger or low pressure (LP) cylinder where it does further work before exhausting to condenser or atmosphere.

Condenser A chamber where exhaust steam is cooled and converted to water thus creating a vacuum.

Corliss Valve A semi-rotary or rocking valve controlling steam admission or exhaust. (Of similar proportions to a rolling pin).

Cornish Boiler A horizontal cylindrical shell boiler with one internal furnace tube and an external system of brickwork flues.

Cut-off The point in the piston stroke at which the admission valve closes.

Double Beat Drop Valve A circular valve having two seats which falls vertically to close, controlling steam admission or exhaust. Also known as a Cornish valve.

Double Acting An engine in which steam acts alternately on each side of the piston and does work when the piston is moving in both directions.

Eccentric or Eccentric Sheave A disc fixed off centre on the engine crankshaft. Provides reciprocating motion for the valve gear.

Eccentric Strap A collar fitting around the eccentric sheave which transmits reciprocating motion to the valve gear.

Economiser A system of tubes set in the main flue from a boiler through which the boiler feed water is passed to extract heat from the flue gases and raise its temperature before entering the boiler.

Expansion Slide Valve A slide valve with an auxiliary valve on the back controlling the cut-off. May be adjustable by hand or by the governor.

Extraction Engine Usually a compound engine where some steam is bled off for other purposes as it exhausts from the HP cylinder.

Governor A mechanical device driven by the engine which regulates speed by controlling the amount of steam admitted to the engine cylinder.

Head Pressure due to height of water above a pump plus the frictional losses in the delivery pipework.

Hot Well A chamber into which the condensate from the condenser is discharged. The boiler feed pump often draws its supply from this source thus returning warm water to the boiler.

Lancashire Boiler As a Cornish boiler but with two internal furnace tubes.

Parallel Motion A system of geometric linkages coupling the piston rod to the beam engine. The linkage guides the piston rod in a straight line. Used also on some vertical engines.

Piston Drop Valve A vertically reciprocating valve bobbin shaped, but with one head only. Falls to close. Controls steam admission or exhaust.

Piston Valve A bobbin shaped reciprocating valve performing the same function as a slide valve.

Ram Pump Sometimes known as a force pump or a plunger pump. The pump piston or ram is a solid piece of metal which by its movement in the pump cylinder or barrel forces water through the delivery pipe.

Receiver A vessel or chamber for holding exhaust steam.

Re-heater A tubular heat exchanger through which superheated steam to the engine and steam from HP to LP cylinder is passed without coming into actual contact. Some heat is taken from the superheated steam to dry the steam passing to the LP cylinder.

Single Acting An engine in which steam acts only on one side of the piston and which does work when the piston is moving in one direction only.

Slide Valve A sliding 'D'-shaped valve controlling steam admission and exhaust to and from the cylinder.

Steam Chest The housing for the slide or piston valve.

Superheater A bank of small tubes set in the boiler flue through which steam is passed on its way from boiler to engine. Heat is absorbed from the flue gases raising the temperature of the steam and evaporating moisture particles.

Trip Gear A mechanism which releases a Corliss or drop type admission valve allowing it to be closed by a spring or other device. Usually controlled by the governor thereby controlling cut-off and speed.

Triple Expansion An engine with three (or more) cylinders of increasing size. Steam is passed from one to the other — high pressure (HP), intermediate pressure (IP), and low pressure (LP).

The following terms apply almost entirely to non-rotative beam pumping engines:

Balance Bob A centrally pivotted beam, weighted at one end and coupled to the pump rods in a mine shaft at the other. Its purpose was to partly counterbalance the enormous weight of the pump rods.

Equilibrium Valve A valve which allows steam to pass from the top side of the piston to the underside, equalising the pressure on both sides of the piston and putting it in equilibrium.

Handles Specially shaped arms which, through linkages, operate the various valves controlling steam admission, exhaust, etc. They are operated by the plug rod when the engine is running and, when the engine is being started, by hand.

Nozzles A term used in Cornwall for the housing or chest containing Cornish type double-beat valves.

Perpendicular Pipe A vertical pipe which conveys equilibrium steam from the top of the cylinder to the bottom.

Plug Rod A vertical rod attached to the beam which by means of 'tappets' operates the 'handles' of the valves controlling steam admission, exhaust, etc.

Steam Horn A particularly Cornish term for the steam inlet valve handle. Usually of a curly shape like a ram's horn, hence the name.

Tappets Shaped wooden slides clamped to the plug rod which strike or release the 'handles' as the plug rod rises and falls.

bhp or **hp** Brake horse power — the power available at the crankshaft, being ihp less losses due to friction etc within the engine.

gph Gallons per hour.

gpm Gallons per minute.

ihp Indicated horse power — the power developed in the engine cylinder.

mgd Million gallons per day.

psi Pounds per square inch pressure above the pressure of the atmosphere — ie 'gauge' pressure.

rpm Revolutions per minute.

spm Working strokes per minute.

Note that the size of steam engines is usually that of the cylinder/s expressed as internal bore × stroke (both in inches). The term '60 in engine' denotes an engine with a steam cylinder of 60 in internal diameter. The specification for each engine listed includes (where known) the manufacturer and date, size, speed, type of valve gear, boilers, etc.

Engines are listed in alphabetical order of sites in each section, but where an on-site preservation has an associated museum collection then the engines moved to that site will be found in the 'on-site' section of the book.

1 ON SITE PRESERVATION
Public Access on a Regular Basis

ALL SAINTS BREWERY, Stamford, Lincs

INVERTED VERTICAL SINGLE CYLINDER
MILL ENGINE
Marshall & Sons, Gainsborough, 1910, 7 in ×
10 in, slide valve, Pickering governor. Cornish
boiler, 5 ft 6 in × 18 ft by Gimson & Co,
Leicester.

Eastern England was prolific in engine builders, and although their engines were usually
less grand than Lancashire and Yorkshire built
engines their use was much more widespread.
In small powers engines could be obtained
virtually 'off the shelf'.

The All Saint's Brewery engine is typical of
the almost mass produced engines made for

*All Saint's Brewery. This small Marshall
inverted vertical engine is typical of the 'donkey
engines' which performed the menial tasks of
industry.*

use at home and abroad. It was obtained
second-hand in 1947 to replace an old vertical
engine part of which is still in position. Drive
from the Marshall engine is by belt from a
pulley on the crankshaft to a similar pulley
which replaced the crank on the crankshaft of
the old engine. The boiler appears to be the
second on the site and latterly was fitted with a
Hodgkinson underfeed stoker and automatic
controls. The circular section brick chimney
standing on a square base is dated 1876.

Methods of beer making had changed little
here since 1876, even the old beer coolers were
in use, until the need to replace the boiler in
1974 caused closure. The brewery is being
developed as a museum of brewing and is open
April to September, Wednesdays to Sunday
and Bank Holidays.

CEFN COED COAL AND STEAM CENTRE,
Blaenant Colliery, Crynant, West
Glamorgan

TWIN CYLINDER HORIZONTAL COLLIERY
WINDING ENGINE
Worsley Mesnes Ironworks, Wigan, 1927,
32 in × 60 in, drop valve inlet, Corliss valve
exhaust, Gooch valve gear, trunk crosshead
guides, parallel drum 16 ft diameter, caliper
brakes, Worsley Mesnes overwind/overspeed
controller, six Lancashire boilers, two Weir
boiler feed pumps.

Preserved colliery winding engines are few,
but a determined attempt is being made in
South Wales to preserve a selection of engines
in situ as old collieries are abandoned.

The Cefn Coed engine is modern for a steam
winder and the inlet drop valves are fitted with
trip gear controlled by a governor. As the
engine accelerated the governor caused the trip
gear to release the inlet valves progressively
earlier in the stroke thus ensuring maximum
possible expansion of steam in the cylinders.
Significant economies in steam were obtained
with this method of operation.

The Cefn Coed shaft was 800 yd deep and

15

the engine would be expected to perform about fifty winds per hour from this depth. The severity of the duty is reflected in the massive construction of the engine. The Worsley Mesnes Melling's controller operated pneumatically and prevented overwinding. By the operation of a cock by the winding engineman the engine was controlled at a lower speed for winding men than for mineral and the speed approaching 'bank' was severely limited. Outside the engine house near the shaft top is a single cylinder horizontal engine by Llewelyn & Cubitt and made in the Rhondda. This drove the capstan used for rope changing and other maintenance work in the shaft.

The colliery is open to the public each week from Thursday to Monday inclusive, and is signposted from the Heads of the Valleys road A465.

Cefn Coed (Blaenant) Colliery. Worsley Mesnes ▲ winding engine of 1927, the massive proportions being typical of latter steam winders. Note the governor controlling the trip gear on the inlet valves.

DEVON COLLIERY, New Sauchie, Alloa

CORNISH PUMPING ENGINE
Neilson & Co, Glasgow, 1854

Only the beam and top section of the pump rod remain of this engine, but it has been retained as a monument in part of a land reclamation scheme.

Cefn Coed (Blaenant) Colliery. Shown here is the method of operating inlet and exhaust valves from a wrist plate, and an array of Worsley Mesnes auxiliaries: Melling's controller, brake engine, and reversing engine.

BRIGHTON AND HOVE ENGINEERIUM
Goldstone Pumping Station, Nevill Road, Hove, Sussex

WOOLF COMPOUND WATERWORKS PUMPING ENGINES (2)

No 1 Engine: Easton & Amos, London, 1866, slide valves, twin plate steel beam, Two bucket pumps 33 in × 30 in stroke in well, 160 ft to well head, double acting bucket and plunger pump to high level service reservoirs, 150,000gph, 130hp, 12rpm, jet condenser.

No 2 Engine: Eastons & Anderson, London & Erith, 1875, 28 in × 64¾ in (HP), 46 in × x 96 in (LP), Meyer expansion slide valves (hand adjusted) on HP, simple slide valve on LP, Porter governor, twin plate steel beam, flywheel 23ft 6in diameter, bucket pumps in well, 150ft to well head, double-acting bucket and plunger pump to service reservoir, 450ft head, 125,000gph, 150hp, 16rpm, jet condenser.

Boilers: Four Lancashire by Yates & Thom, Blackburn, 1934, 75psi, Green's economisers, superheaters. Two twin-cylinder 'Cameron' boiler feed pumps by Frank Pearn & Co, Manchester.

The purpose of Goldstone pumping station was to extract water from the underlying chalk. No 1 engine, which is not at present in working order but is being restored, worked for 84 years. During its working life a disc crank, which is still in position, was added to the end of the crankshaft. This drove a force pump to supply a new mid-level service reservoir. The arrangement was not very successful and the pump was subsequently removed. Unusual for its period is the steel plate beam but, in other respects the engine is typical of waterworks practice of the time. The engine is house built with a fine entablature supported under the beam trunnions by Grecian style cast-iron columns.

No 2 engine worked until 1954 and after lying unused for some 20 years was restored to working condition in 1975-6. There are many similarities to No 1 engine but there are also important differences, no doubt reflecting the influence of Anderson in the design of the second engine. As with No 1 engine a crank driven force pump was added to the outer end of the crankshaft and accommodated in a separate small building adjacent to the engine house, and in the same way was later removed.

The boiler house is located between the two engine houses and together with the 120ft ornamental square chimney is original. The

Goldstone No 2. The beam chamber. The beam is made up from two steel plates. Note the decortive guard railings.

boiler plant however is by steam standards quite modern. Yates & Thom, who were familiar as engine builders in the northern textile mills, also had a good boiler trade and manufacture continued long after engine building ceased. Economisers and super-heaters add greatly to the efficiency of the plant and a delightful touch is the little single-cylinder horizontal engine which drives the economiser scraper gear.

Goldstone has a workshop still very much in use, sufficiently equipped to carry out repairs on engines and pumps. The machinery driven by lineshafts, pulleys and belts can still be powered by a single cylinder horizontal slide valve engine. With a 9 in × 18 in cylinder it was made by Eastons & Amos and brought to Goldstone second-hand about 1875.

The museum houses a vast collection of stationary steam engines, together with internal combustion, hot air engines, and traction and portable engines. Additionally there is a large number of superb models on display. One can only appreciate this collection by a visit, and a complete description of all the exhibits would require a full volume in itself. Only three stationary engines, which are regularly run under steam, are described here.

Goldstone No 2. Looking down from the packing floor. Note the Porter governor.

Brighton & Hove Engineerium. The lightness of construction of this French Corliss engine is apparent. The American design influence was strong in this engine.

This engine was built in close co-operation
with the Corliss company of the USA, and the
girder bed and apparent lightness of construction emphasize the American influence. The
engine gained a Gold Medal at the 1889 Paris
Exhibition. Subsequently it was installed in a
Paris hospital where it drove a generator by a
belt from the flywheel. Eventually becoming
redundant it was moved to the Engineerium in
1975-6.

The Corliss valves are driven from a single
wrist-plate oscillated by a crankshaft-mounted
eccentric. Strange to British eyes is the wrist
plate and trip gear fitted as part of the governor
assembly and not on the side of the cylinder.
The condenser is below floor level in front of
the cylinder with the air pump driven by rod
and linkage from the main crankpin. This
again appears unusual to those used to seeing
the air pump drive taken from crosshead or tail
rod.

The engine is typical of small vertical engines
with forked connecting rod, and in this case the
crankshaft bearings are fitted on an entablature
supported by four cast-iron columns. The
engine is now fully restored and is regularly
demonstrated under steam.

Lincolnshire and East Anglia were the homes
of a host of engine builders, whose products
embraced stationary, portable, marine, traction and a few locomotive engines. Marshalls
were very prolific and small inverted vertical
engines such as this were built for stock and
sold 'off the shelf', both for home use and
abroad. The design of the engine with slide
valve, substantial bottle-shaped frame and
Pickering governor is typical of East of
England manufacturers generally.

The Engineerium is open daily throughout
the year except Christmas Day. No 2 engine is
steamed every weekend and Bank Holidays.

*Brighton & Hove Engineerium. A small vertical
engine with four columns and independent of the
engine house.*

BROOMY HILL WATERWORKS, Hereford

This triple expansion engine replaced two
beam engines and its function was to pump
water from the River Wye to the treatment
works on Broomy Hill. The pumps drew from
a well or sump into which river water flowed.
Three ram pumps are driven by side rods from
the engine crossheads and the connecting rods
are fixed to the lower or pump crossheads and
drive upwards to the crankshaft. From the
middle pump a yoke is coupled to two small
ram pumps which formerly delivered filtered
water to a water tower for high level service.
The bulk of the treated water was supplied to
the city by gravity from the treatment works.

Broomy Hill. General view of triple expansion pumping engine. Note the transfer pipe between HP and IP cylinders and the re-heater between IP and LP cylinders.

The engine exhausts to a jet condenser and to improve efficiency reheat is applied to the steam between IP and LP stages. The condenser air pump is driven by an eccentric from the crankshaft and a boiler feed pump is driven by an eccentric on an extension to the crankshaft. The small ram pumps had become inadequate for the high level service by 1906 and a twin cylinder inverted vertical pumping engine was obtained from Worth, Mackenzie for this duty. This engine very much resembles a Cameron type pump but is fitted with a jet condenser to improve efficiency.

The waterworks is open each weekend and Bank Holidays. The small engine is usually run on compressed air, but both engines are run under steam on certain weekends and on Bank Holidays.

CHATTERLEY-WHITFIELD COLLIERY MUSEUM Tunstall, Stoke on Trent, Staffs.

> TWIN CYLINDER HORIZONTAL COLLIERY WINDING ENGINE
> Worsley Mesnes Ironworks, Wigan, 1914, 36 in × 72 in, drop valve inlet, Corliss valve exhaust, Gooch valve gear, trunk crosshead guides, bi-cylindro-conical drum 14-20 ft diameter, caliper brakes, Worsley Mesnes (Melling's) controller.

Chatterley-Whitfield Colliery is the first mining museum to be established where the public have access to underground workings. Worsley Mesnes Ironworks were prolific builders and re-builders of colliery winding engines but only two of their engines are at present in preservation although preserved colliery winding engines are quite rare in any event.

The bi-cylindro-conical drum was used at deep shafts. It reduced the starting torque, assisted acceleration, and at the end of the wind assisted retardation. The 'drop' valves with trip gear operated by a governor progressively reduced the cut-off as the engine accelerated. In railway terms the engine was automatically 'notched up'. These two features of drum and trip gear gave the most economical working possible with winding engines. In a typical winding cycle the engine would commence the wind at 85 per cent cut-off. This would be

Chatterley-Whitfield Colliery. The valve gear is on the outside of the engine and the eccentrics are mounted on stub shafts driven by drag links from the crankpins. The valves are operated by rods from an oscillating wrist plate.

progressively reduced to 20 per cent or less at about half wind. Just beyond half wind steam would be shut off and the engine would coast up to the last few revolutions. Here the engine would be put in reverse and finally steam would be applied against the pistons to bring the cages to decking level. The brakes would then be used to 'spot' the cages accurately at decking level. All this would be accomplished in less than a minute and even at the deepest shafts fifty winds per hour would be made, inclusive of changing the tubs at each wind. A very severe duty both for engine and enginemen and one which by its very nature ruined efficiency. A winding engine even with a trip gear could quite easily take five times as much steam per horse power as a compound mill engine. Large winding engines usually exhausted to low pressure steam accumulators supplying mixed pressure turbines for generating or air compressing, to improve the overall efficiency of the steam plant.

The boilers at Chatterley-Whitfield achieved some fame for they were 10 ft diameter Lanca-shire boilers — an unusually large size, the normal maximum being 9 ft.

The colliery is open to the public Tuesday to Sunday inclusive plus the summer Bank Holidays. Times are approximately 10.00 a.m. until 4.30 p.m.

Chatterley-Whitfield Colliery. The massive construction of the whole engine is evident when looking from the crankshaft end. The drag link drive to the valve gear is also visible.

COLEHAM PUMPING STATION, Shrewsbury

WOOLF COMPOUND SEWAGE WORKS PUMP-
ING ENGINES (2)
W. Renshaw & Co, Stoke-on-Trent, 1900, 13 in
× 46 in (HP), 21 in × 54 in (LP), divided slide
valves (HP), Meyer expansion gear (hand
adjusted); double beat 'Cornish' valves LP,
twin plate steel beam. Two plunger type
sewage pumps. Two Cornish boilers, 90 psi.
'Prior' underfeed stokers.

Built at a time when beam engine construction
was coming to an end, the Coleham engines,
while house-built, are examples of the smaller
type of engine. The sewage pumps are in a deep
basement located one each side of the beam
fulcrum. As the pumps are quite close to the
beam pivot the pump rods are coupled directly
to the beam without parallel motion.

The valve gear takes its motion from an
underfloor layshaft driven by bevel gearing
from the crankshaft. The HP main slide valve
is operated by an eccentric and rocker arm and
the LP valves by cam and roller followers. The
valve rods push up on the valve handles. The
expansion valve on the HP cylinder is driven
by a link from the beam. The LP valves are
housed in chests at each end of the cylinder
connected by two perpendicular pipes. These
pipes have copper bellows to take up expansion
and contraction. Exhaust steam passed to a
condenser and feed water was supplied to the
boilers by an engine driven pump. An injector
was provided as standby boiler feed.

*Coleham. Steel-plate beam and parallel motion
linkage.*

*Coleham. High pressure steam chest (right) and
top and bottom nozzles of the low pressure
cylinder. The valve levers are pushed up by the
rods from the underfloor cams to open the valves.*

Electric pumps replaced the engines in 1969
and Shrewsbury Museums now maintain the
engines as static exhibits. One engine may be
turned slowly by an electric motor geared into
the original barring engine. Access is on
Wednesday and Friday afternoons throughout the year.

CROFTON PUMPING STATION,
Great Bedwyn, Wilts

CORNISH CANAL PUMPING ENGINE
No 1 Engine: Boulton & Watt, Birmingham,
1812, 42 in × 7 ft 9 in equal beam, 11 spm, 20 psi.
Bucket pump 30 in × 7 ft 9 in. 3 mgd reservoir to
canal summit level.

The purpose of the Crofton Pumping Station
is to supply water from a natural source to the
summit level of the Kennet & Avon canal.
Water is delivered from the pumping station to
the summit by a specially constructed leat.
Work on the pumping station started in 1800,
John Rennie being the engineer. Pumping
started in 1809 and this engine was the second
to be installed. As built both engines worked at
low pressure and took steam from three
'waggon-top' boilers which stood outside.

The beam consists of two cast-iron plates
with the parallel motion loops fitted outside.
Each end of the beam has parallel motion as the
pump rod is short. The pump which is a large
example of the old farmyard type is at the
bottom of a shaft connected by a culvert to the
reservoir. With this type of pump delivery is on
the 'up' or indoor stroke. Originally the engine
was 8 ft stroke but at some later date it was
shortened to 7 ft 9 in.

In pursuit of economy the engine was rebuilt
in 1844 to work on the Cornish system with
steam at 20 psi supplied by three Cornish
boilers. New valve gear was fitted, which
although similar to normal Cornish gear has no
cataract, but the interlocking quadrants or
scoggans and latch gear ensure the correct
cycle of operation. Following the rebuild in
1844 the engine worked until 1958. Two
Lancashire boilers made at Swindon Works
replaced the Cornish boilers in 1905. Although
made for only 20 psi these boilers, 7 ft 6 in ×
27 ft, are very strongly built and have corrugated furnace tubes. The state of the chimney in
1958 necessitated removal of the top 20 ft
spoiling the draught so that insufficient steam
was maintained. Electric pumps were then
installed.

The Crofton Pumping Station Trust took
over the engine house in 1968 and restoration
of buildings, engines and boilers was commenced. No 1 engine was the first to be
restored and can once again pump water into
the canal. It is believed to be the oldest working
steam engine in the world.

*Crofton. Beam of the 1812 Boulton & Watt
engine. The beam chamber is well lit by numerous
small Georgian windows and there is plenty of
timber, in contrast to the Kew Bridge engine
houses.*

*Crofton. Parallel motion beam loops of the
Boulton & Watt engine. Features to note are that
they are outside the beam plates, the piston rod
cap is cottered to the piston rod. An old 'suet'
lubricator for animal fat is fitted on the cylinder
top cover.*

Crofton. GWR Swindon-built Lancashire boiler. ▲
*Note the corrugated furnace tubes and the large
nuts securing longitudinal stay rods. An enorm-
ously strong boiler for a mere 20psi working
pressure.*

◄ *Crofton. Valve gear of the Harvey engine. The
tappet on the descending plug rod has just engaged
with the steam horn and closed the admission
valve.*

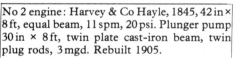

No 2 engine: Harvey & Co Hayle, 1845, 42 in ×
8 ft, equal beam, 11 spm, 20 psi. Plunger pump
30 in × 8 ft, twin plate cast-iron beam, twin
plug rods, 3 mgd. Rebuilt 1905.

In further pursuit of economy the 1809 engine
was removed in 1845 and replaced by a Sims'
combined engine. The Sims engine which had
a brief spell of popularity in Cornwall was a
form of tandem compound and had a large low
pressure cylinder beneath the normal one. The
pistons were connected by a common piston
rod. At Crofton the engine gave so much
trouble that it was hardly ever used and was
later largely dismantled. In 1905 however the
Great Western Railway who had become
owners of the Kennet & Avon canal, had the
engine rebuilt as a normal 42 in Cornish,
although as with the Boulton & Watt engine no
cataract is fitted. It may be thought strange
that the GWR should pay such attention to
Crofton but the canal was also used as a water
supply for locomotives.

The beam of the Harvey engine is noticeably
lighter than its Boulton & Watt partner and in
Cornish manner the plates are set wider apart
with the parallel motion loops between.

Parallel motion is fitted to both ends of the
beam. The pump being of the plunger type
delivers water on the outdoor stroke. Below the
floor is the condenser and air pump. The air
pump discharges into a hot well from which
the boiler feed pump (also below floor level)
draws its supply. A third pump delivers surplus water from the hot well into a small
reservoir or into the canal feeder. Cooling
water for the condenser is drawn from a cold
tank supplied by the main pump. These
arrangements also apply to the Boulton & Watt
engine. For feeding the boilers when the
engines are not running a Worthington-
Simpson 'Duplex' horizontal steam pump has
been installed. The Harvey engine was in use
until 1952 and has now been restored and is
regularly steamed along with the Boulton &
Watt engine.

The Pumping Station is open every weekend during the summer months and the
engines are operated in steam on about six
weekends in the year. Full details are obtainable from the Crofton Society, 273 East
Grafton, Burbage, Wiltshire.

EASTNEY PUMPING STATION, Portsmouth

> WOOLF COMPOUND SEWAGE WORKS PUMP-
> ING ENGINES (2)
> James Watt & Co, Birmingham, 1886. 20 in ×
> 54 in (HP), 30 in × 72 in (LP). Watt-type
> governor, twin plate cast-iron beam 23 ft long,
> 3 ft 6 in max depth, flywheel 15 ft diameter.
> Two plunger pumps 30 in × 39 in, 500,000 gph,
> 125 hp, 20 rpm, 80 psi.

Portsea Island on which Portsmouth is situated is low lying and impossible to drain properly by sewers running directly into the sea. A limited pumping scheme was installed in 1868 but this soon became inadequate. The Watt engines were installed to pump from the sewer outfall to storage tanks above sea level from which sewage could be rapidly discharged.

The engines are house-built, the entablature being built into the engine house walls with additional support from cast-iron columns under the beam trunnions. Below floor level on each side of the beam fulcrum are the sewage pumps, driven by rods from the beam. The pumps are relatively close to the beam centre and the rods do not need parallel motion as the arc described by the fixing point is small. The piston rods are guided by parallel motion in the usual way. Also below the floor are the condenser, air pump, boiler feed pump, and condenser cooling water pump. All the auxiliary pumps are operated by rods from the beam.

As was quite usual with sewage works engines, the governor was for overspeed protection only, the speed of the engine being regulated by a hand valve to suit the flow of sewage. If necessary the engines could be run up to 24 rpm. Steam was supplied to the engines by four 7 ft × 27 ft Lancashire boilers but these have now gone. Steam for running under demonstration is now supplied by two locomotive type boilers. Engine house, boiler house and chimney are constructed in red brick although the chimney was severely truncated after shut-down of the engines. The style of the engine and boiler houses is best described as 'non-conformist ecclesiastical' often adopted by public utilities in Victorian times.

Electric pumps largely replaced the engines in 1937 but they were held in reserve until 1954. In due course the engines passed to the Portsmouth City Museums and restoration was commenced in 1968. They are now open to the public daily, and one engine can be run in steam. Demonstrations in steam are given at intervals, and details of these should be obtained from Portsmouth City Museums.

> GRASSHOPPER WATERWORKS PUMPING
> ENGINE
> Easton, Amos & Anderson, c1860s, 12 in ×
> 16 in.

This engine, from the Havant Works of the Portsmouth Waterworks Company has been re-erected at Eastney and will be made workable.

EAST POOL MINE, Redruth, Cornwall

> CORNISH WHIM ENGINE,
> MICHELL'S 30 inch
> Holman Bros, Camborne, 1887, double acting,
> 30 in × 9 ft, 27 rpm, link-motion reversing gear,
> double-beat valves, twin winding drums,
> round steel ropes, rope speed 1,000 ft per min.

The typical Cornish 'whim' or winding engine was built in similar manner to the pumping engine with the beam trunnions supported by the front wall of the engine house. The connecting or 'sweep' rod, flywheel and winding

East Pool Whim. The typical Cornish whim or winding engine with flywheel, winding drum and connecting or sweep rod all outdoors. The boiler is in the lean-to alongside.

drums were outdoors. Beam engines for winding survived much longer in Cornwall than in the coal mining districts. The slow winding speed was not so important as the amount of mineral wound was relatively small. Often quick winding was an impossibility due to the crookedness of the shafts sunk to follow the metal lode rather than truly vertical. Ore was wound in egg shaped kibbles which bumped around in the shaft. Skips and cages were not generally introduced until late in the Cornish mining era. The rapidity of Michell's engine reflects the improvements which had been made in winding techniques by the time this engine was installed.

Early whim engines often used the single acting Cornish steam cycle but later engines were double acting. Michell's was the last beam whim to be built for a Cornish mine and is the last of traditional construction to remain in situ. Cornish whim engines condensed their exhaust steam and on this engine the air pump and boiler feed pump are operated by rods from the outdoor end of the beam. The beam itself is built up from two cast iron plates in normal Cornish manner.

The engine was first preserved by the Cornish Engines Preservation Society and is now in the care of the National Trust. Access is daily April-Oct. The engine stands by the A30 Redruth to Camborne road.

East Pool Whim. The bottom chamber or driving floor showing the cylinder, bottom nozzles and starting valve.

CORNISH PUMPING ENGINE,
TAYLOR'S 90 inch
Harvey & Co, Hayle 1892. 90 in × 10/9 ft. 5 spm, 450 gpm from 1,700 feet. Seven pump lifts, six of 18 in, one of 16 in. Cast-iron beam 33 ft 3 in long by 8 ft 6 in deep.

Cornish pumping engines were always designated for size by the internal diameter of the cylinder and in Cornwall each mine shaft had a name. 'Taylor's 90 inch' means a pumping engine with a 90 in cylinder at Taylor' shaft. This engine is the largest surviving on a Cornish mine and is also quite a late example. Built originally for Carn Brae Mines it was commissioned in 1893. Unusual wrought iron pump rods 8 in diameter were used for the first 113 fathoms vertical section of the shaft and

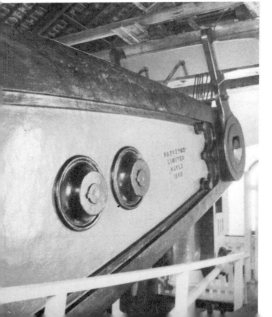

East Pool, Taylor's 90 inch. The 'bob' weighs 52 tons and is one of the largest made. Note the parallel motion loops inside the beam plates and the floating gudgeons – all typical Cornish practice.

the usual wooden rods 15 in square reducing to 13 in working on rollers were used in the subsequent 209 fathoms of angled or 'underlie' shaft. The iron pump rods gave a lot of trouble and were replaced by wooden rods in 1914. At Carn Brae a steam pressure of 45 psi was used and cut-off was at one quarter stroke. Due to mine closures the engine was rendered idle in 1915.

In April and May 1921 a series of disastrous collapses of the workings at East Pool Mine made the mine unworkable. To continue the extraction of known reserves a new shaft was necessary and this was sunk to 1,700 feet by 1924. To drain the mine the 90 in engine was brought from Carn Brae and re-erected at the new Taylor's shaft. Wooden pump rods were used throughout the shaft, 20 in square at the surface and reducing to 16 in at the bottom lift. In 1946 the load on the engine was reduced as the pumping level was brought up to 1,034 feet from the surface.

East Pool, Taylor's 90 inch. The middle chamber ▲ *showing the cylinder top and top nozzles.*

The engine is probably the heaviest for its size ever built, the twin plate beam alone weighing 52 tons. The indoor end of the beam is 1 ft 9 in longer than the outdoor end giving the shorter stroke in the shaft. As usual with large engines two perpendicular pipes are provided and the valve gear is operated by twin plug rods. Two cataracts are fitted giving a pause at the end of indoor and outdoor strokes. The designer of the engine was Nicholas Trestrail.

About 1938 a main pump rod broke resulting in a bowed piston rod and the bob was lifted out of its trunnions or stools. Not long before the engine ceased work the winding headgear over the shaft collapsed taking much of the engine house roof with it. The beam worked in the open air until repairs were carried out. In 1946 a new surface balance bob was provided this being a steel plate main beam from the last Cornish engine to be built (for Goonbarrow clayworks in 1914) which had been scrapped about this time. A box was added to this beam to carry scrap iron for counterweighting.

While still working the engine was purchased by the Cornish Engines Preservation Society by means of a donation from Mr. Greville Bath of Florida, so that when working

East Pool, Taylor's 90 inch. The valve gear with the bottom or exhaust nozzle, and the twin perpendicular pipes seen behind. The slotted vertical rods are controlled by the cataracts and move upwards to release the scoggans holding the valves closed. The left-hand rod releases the inlet and exhaust valves and the right-hand the equilibrium valve.

ceased on 28 September 1954 its future was assured. Eventually the engine was taken over by the National Trust and is now open to the public daily during the summer months. The engine house is located north of the A 30 Redruth to Camborne road. Enquiries should be directed to the National Trust, Warren Davis, Saltram, Plympton, Plymouth, Devon.

'THE ENGINE HOUSE',
Burgess Road, Nottingham

SINGLE CYLINDER HORIZONTAL ENGINE
Tangyes, Birmingham, c 1850s.

Preserved in situ seems a strange heading for an engine preserved in a public house. Nevertheless it is a fact for the pub is part of an old brickworks. The engine performed its normal duties until 1966. Access is during 'opening hours' for the price of a pint!

ERDDIG ESTATE, Wrexham, Clwyd

SINGLE CYLINDER VERTICAL ENGINE
Maker unknown, c 1861

Like many estate engines this drove the sawmill. Economy of operation was achieved by burning waste wood.

The estate is now a National Trust property and times of opening are available from any National Trust office.

GLENRUTHVEN MILL, R. White & Sons (1929) Ltd, Auchterarder, Perthshire

TANDEM COMPOUND HORIZONTAL MILL ENGINE
Maker unknown c 1873, 10½ in (HP), 20 in (LP) × 30 in, slide valves. Pickering governor, jet condenser, belt drive to mill, 64 rpm, 60 psi. Cornish boiler by Penman & Co, Glasgow, 1949.

This very plain and simple engine represents an early generation of compound horizontal engines. Developing about 65 ihp, it performed with great reliability. Although over 40 years old when brought to this mill it ran for another 60 years and lost only two days production in that time.

The mill itself was built about 1870 and was equipped with looms by the Anderston Foundry, Glasgow. Originally there were about 100 and although some are still in situ, in recent years their use declined and finally ceased altogether in 1980. Production continues on a small number of modern electrically driven looms.

Glenruthven Mill. An old-time tandem compound engine with wood lagged cylinders, flat bed and fish bellied slide bars.

The engine driving this historic machinery was installed about 1919 to replace a smaller engine and is believed to have come from a sawmill in the Glasgow area. The high pressure cylinder is behind the low pressure and has the condenser mounted alongside. Typical of older horizontal engines is the flat bed-plate and fish-bellied slide bars. The flywheel is plain with barring holes around the rim. Drive is taken from a separate pulley alongside the flywheel. At the crankshaft end of the bed plate is the boiler feed pump and this and the condenser air pump are driven by a side rod from the crosshead. A throttle governor valve controls the speed. The cylinders retain the original wood strip lagging which gives an appropriate air of antiquity.

Access is Monday to Thursday and Friday mornings with the usual Scottish hour for lunch from 12.30. Also beware the Scottish public holidays such as Victoria Day!

KEW BRIDGE PUMPING STATION,
Brentford, Middlesex

CORNISH WATERWORKS PUMPING ENGINE
MAUDSLAY 65 inch
Maudslay, Sons & Field, London 1837, 65 in ×
8 ft equal beam, twin-plate cast iron beam,
twin perpendicular pipes, twin plug rods,
single cataract, 40 psi, 10 spm, 2½ mgd.

The Maudslay engine was the first to work at
Kew Bridge. This firm were pioneers in the
development of machine tools and they also
built marine engines. Although this is the last
of Maudslay's large engines to survive very
little of the original does in fact remain, as the
cylinder, valves and valve gear, pump and one
of the beam plates were all replaced at various
times in the nineteenth century. King posts
and bridles were fitted to the beam in 1862, but
the beam plates fractured in 1888. The beam
plates are arranged in Cornish fashion with
the parallel motion loops inside. The cylinder
and perpendicular pipes have fluted casings
and the nozzles are also decorated, but the
engine as a whole is plainer than the Cornish
built ones.

Those with an eye for detail will notice that
the piston rod cap to which the parallel motion
loops are attached is fixed to the piston rod by a
cotter. The Cornish built engines have a
shoulder inside the cap and a groove in the
piston rod in which the two halves of a C-ring
engage. If the beam tried to overtake the piston
rod, as it would try to do if the piston hit the
cylinder bottom, it could in fact do so.
Hopefully the movement of the beam would be
arrested by the spring beams and damage to

the cylinder minimised, as the blow of the
piston would be lessened. The conditions
could, and did, occur if there was a sudden loss
of load. The pump itself is concealed in what
appears to be a large wooden tank but which is
in fact cast iron.

*Kew, Maudsday 65in. Valve gear arranged in
conventional Cornish manner on this London-
built engine with steam, equilibrium and exhaust
arbors equally spaced.*

*Kew. Cylinder top of the Bull 70in and the beam
of the Maudslay 65in.*

CORNISH WATERWORKS PUMPING ENGINE
BOULTON & WATT 64 inch
Boulton & Watt, Soho Works, Birmingham,
1820; rebuilt 1848. 64 in × 8 ft equal beam,
10 spm, 2½ mgd, 40 psi.

This engine and its companion were removed to Kew Bridge in 1839 from Chelsea waterworks. As built the engine worked at the low pressure of 4½ psi, and a rebuild in 1848 involved the fitting of new valve gear so that the engine could work on the Cornish principle using high pressure steam. Pump valves, balance weight, cataract and auxiliary pumps are also of this date.

One of the most noticeable differences between this and the Cornish built engines is that the beam is made of two cast iron plates, but fixed close together with the parallel motion loops fitted outside. The valve gear is differently arranged also with the steam arbor fixed very high and having only very functional steam horns. A single plug rod operates the valve gear and the cataract stands on the driving floor near the cylinder. Below floor under the driver's feet are the condenser and the air pump.

The engine worked until 1944, apparently without mishap, but the sister engine broke its beam in 1862. King posts and bridles were then fitted to the beam. The sister engine was removed in 1946 and following this the driving floor had some plates removed to expose the pump of the remaining engine. With one engine gone it is possible to stand back and see the whole of the engine in action. This was the first engine to be restored and was steamed again on 8 November 1975.

The house containing this engine and the Maudslay and Bull engines is built in brick in the Georgian style and access to the various engine floors is by a York stone staircase with landing doors off. Every effort was made towards a fireproof building. A minimum of wood was used and the roof is an ingenious structure of wrought iron strips.

Kew, Boulton & Watt 64in. The pump rod with its lead filled forcing weight. Note that parallel motion is necessary on the pump rod of a waterworks Cornish engine.

Kew, Boulton & Watt 64in. The beam with king post and bridle. Note the parallel motion loops fitted outside the beam plates.

The efficiency of the large Cornish pumping engines attracted the attention of the wealthy waterworks companies in the London area. The first Cornish engine to work in a London waterworks was an 80 in started in December 1838 at Old Ford. It had been obtained second hand from Wheal Langford near Callington in Cornwall, having worked only for a few months. After some initial difficulty with the pump clack valves it proved to be highly successful.

With plenty of money available there was no need to buy second-hand and when the Grand Junction Waterworks Company required another engine for Kew Bridge pumping station a brand new one was ordered. This engine was started at Kew Bridge on 30 May 1846 and worked until 31 July 1943. Known when new as the 'Grand Junction Engine' it is possibly the finest and most elegant Cornish engine in existence. At the time of its commissioning it was the largest waterworks engine in the world.

The beam is light (24 tons) for an engine of this size and following Cornish practice the

Kew, Grand Junction 90in. An elegant beam for such a large engine. The strengthening bridles pass around the edges of the beam plates and are tensioned by cottered joints.

Kew, Grand Junction 90in. Cornish valve gear at its most elegant. Note the decorative steam handle or horn on the uppermost arbor. The interlocking scoggans on equilibrium and exhaust arbors are seen nearest the camera. The cataract latches are at the opposite end of the arbors.

parallel motion loops are fitted inside the beam plates. As the pump rod is short it requires to be guided by parallel motion and a massive weight chamber filled with iron forms part of the pump rod to provide the driving force on the outdoor stroke. Originally two cataracts were fitted but later the top handle or equilibrium cataract was removed so that the engine now pauses only at the end of the outdoor stroke. The cataract itself is of elegant design and instead of being concealed below the floor stands near the cylinder on the driving floor. When working at normal speed 6½ million gallons per day were delivered.

The engine house is built in ashlar stone and completely encloses the engine. To provide access to each floor the Copperhouse Foundry supplied a fine cast iron staircase. Although the engine is relatively light in construction it seems to have given little trouble. Harvey & Co gave the engine a general overhaul in 1855 and fitted new pumpwork. The top of the pump is above the driving floor and its action can be clearly seen. King posts and bridles were fitted to the beam in 1862, not because the beam was showing signs of failure but as a precautionary measure following trouble with the beams of other engines at Kew Bridge.

Kew, Grand Junction 90in. Cylinder top cover, top nozzles and, in the background, the massive entablature supporting the beam trunnion bearings. This entablature was usual in waterworks Cornish engines, although the earliest ones did have a masonry cross wall more in accordance with mining practice.

BULL CORNISH WATERWORKS PUMPING ENGINE
BULL 70 inch
Harvey & Co, Hayle, 1855, 70 in × 10 ft, 10 spm, 4·3 mgd, 40 psi.

Edward Bull, a foreman erector for Boulton & Watt in Cornwall invented his own version of pumping engine in 1793. He inverted the cylinder directly over the mine shaft and coupled the piston rod straight on to the 'spears' or pump rods. Bull was successfully prosecuted by Boulton & Watt for infringement of their patent and it was not until much later, long after the inventor's death that Bull engines were built in numbers. The Bull engine worked on the Cornish steam cycle and achieved its greatest popularity outside Cornwall mainly for use at collieries. As can be seen at Kew Bridge the Bull engine occupied less than half the space of a normal Cornish engine but in spite of this was never so popular. The piston rod gland was hard to get at and any shake in the spears was transmitted to the piston rod. The sheer mass of a Cornish engine made it run beautifully smoothly and regulation was easy. The Bull engine at Kew Bridge is a unique survival.

The engine replaced two grasshopper engines alongside the Maudslay 65 inch. Pumps and auxiliaries are concealed in a panelled compartment below the cylinder on what is the driving floor of the Maudslay engine. The driving floor of the Bull engine corresponds to the packing floor of the Maudslay engine. The valve gear, which is the same as a Cornish engine, is operated by a single plug rod which comes up from below floor. A single cataract is fitted. The top of the cylinder projects through into the beam floor of the Maudslay engine.

CORNISH WATERWORKS PUMPING ENGINE
HARVEY 100 inch
Harvey & Co, Hayle, 1869, 100 in × 11 ft, equal beam, twin plate cast-iron beam, twin plug rods, twin perpendicular pipes, 40 psi, 8 spm, 10 mgd.

Harvey & Co supplied many engines to the London waterworks. By 1862 nearly 70 per cent of water consumed in London was pumped by engines built by Harveys. In the 1860s and '70s Harveys ran many of the waterworks engines on contract supplying staff for maintenance and operation.

The Grand Junction Waterworks Company's specification for the 100in called for an engine similar to the Grand Junction 90in but there are many differences. Most obvious is the tremendous weight of the 100in engine and this is particularly so in the case of the beam. The main pump is below driving floor level and the balance weight works through an opening in the floor and nothing can be seen of the pump's operation. The 100in started in

Kew, Harvey 100in. In contrast to the 90 inch next door this engine has a beam of gigantic proportions.

Kew, Harvey 100in. Cornish valve gear. The ▶ cataract latches are clearly seen nearest the camera.

1871 and it was linked to the cataract on the 90 in engine so that they worked in unison. The 90 in had its top handle cataract removed at this time.

The engine house forms an extension of the 90 in house although it is difficult to tell that this is so. Windows in the 90 in house were skilfully modified to form archways giving access to each floor of the 100 in engine. The cast iron staircases made by the Copperhouse Foundry for the 90 in also serve the 100 in but Harveys added a curved extension at the bottom.

In spite of the very heavy construction one side of the beam (nearest the 90 in) cracked in 1879 while the engine was working. Fortunately this was spotted before complete failure and the engine was stopped. A patch was bolted on to the beam plate and king posts and bridles added for additional strength. The bridles on this and the other engines are wrought iron forged to shape and held together by cottered joints which also put on the correct amount of tensioning.

In front of the engine house is the stand-pipe tower. This was erected in 1867 and is nearly 200 ft high. It contains four pipes and the height of water in these pipes provided the pressure for the water mains. Its main function however was to protect the engines by giving them an assured head on the pumps. A sudden loss of load such as could be occasioned by a burst water main is disastrous to a Cornish engine as there is no crank to regulate the piston stroke. Often the piston would smash through the bottom of the cylinder.

The 100 in engine is not yet restored to working order but may be seen at all times the 90 in is working simply by walking through the connecting archways.

Museum exhibits moved to Kew Bridge include:

> TWIN SIX-COLUMN BEAM PUMPING ENGINE
> DANCER'S END PUMPING STATION,
> CHILTERN HILLS WATERWORKS
> Maker obscure, possibly J. C. Kay, Bury, Lancs, 1866, 12 in × 30 in; Meyer expansion slide valves (fixed cut-off), Watt type governor, single plate cast-iron beams, Watt parallel motion, 18 rpm, 250 ft head, 62 psi.

A small self-contained engine with the entablature on each side supported by six cast-iron columns. Each side of the engine drove a well pump by a rod from the indoor end of the beam. The condenser was below the floor with the air pump and auxiliaries driven from the outdoor end of the beam. The engine was dismantled in 1977 and taken to Kew Bridge for re-erection.

> WOOLF COMPOUND ROTATIVE PUMPING ENGINE
> From CLIFTONVILLE WATERWORKS, NORTHAMPTON
> Eastons & Amos, 1863, 17 in × 40 in (HP), 30 in × 60 in (LP), slide valves, single plate cast-iron beam, cruciform connecting rod, Porter type governor.

A house-built engine of fairly small proportions at least for an engine of this type. The engine had been dismantled and put into store in Northampton and was brought to Kew Bridge in 1977. Re-erection was remarkably rapid and the engine was steamed again in February 1978. The method of preservation with the entablature built into brick wall sections shows very well the method of installation of this type of engine while enabling the viewer to see the whole of the engine, something it was impossible to do in its working location. It is interesting to compare this engine with the much larger ones by the same maker at the Brighton & Hove Engineerium.

Kew. Twin six-column beam engine. This view in its working location at Dancer's End shows how this design is completely independent of the engine house.

> INVERTED VERTICAL TRIPLE EXPANSION PUMPING ENGINE
> From SOUTHFIELDS PUMPING STATION, NEWMARKET
> Hathorn, Davey, Leeds, 1910.

Dismantled in 1978 and removed to Kew Bridge for re-erection.

> SINGLE CYLINDER HORIZONTAL ENGINES
> Two small engines, one of which, made by E. Green of Wakefield was formerly used for driving economiser scraper gear.

The Boulton and Watt 64 in and the Grand Junction 90 in are steamed every weekend and Bank Holidays. Details from Kew Bridge Engines Trust, Green Dragon Lane, Brentford, Middlesex.

LEA WOOD PUMPING STATION,
Cromford, Derbyshire

CORNISH CANAL PUMPING ENGINE
Graham & Co, Milton Ironworks, Elsecar, Yorkshire, 1849, 50 in × 10 ft equal beam, plunger pump 56 in × 10 ft, twin plate cast-iron beam, single perpendicular pipe, single plug rod, single cataract, 30 ft lift, 7 spm. Two locomotive type boilers, 40 psi by Midland Railway Derby Works, 1904.

This engine was Works No 57 and as Graham & Co appear to have closed down about 1849 it could possibly have been their last. It is claimed that the Lea Wood engine is the only Cornish-type engine existing which has neither been moved nor modified. Most had a nomadic existance being moved from mine to mine as mineral became exhausted or were altered in some way, or both.

The Lea Wood engine was built to pump water from the River Derwent into the Cromford Canal. The engine is 'all indoors' in an exceptionally fine engine house of local stone. A massive internal cross-wall supports the beam trunnions. The top of the pump is level with the driving floor and the plunger is

Lea Wood. The engine house is attractive, simple in style and has few windows. The boiler house alongside is early 20th-century, but carefully matched in style to the 1849 engine house.

Lea Wood. The beam plates are close together with the parallel motion loops fitted outside. Note also the centre rib cast in the web of the beam plates. All these features were common on engines built outside Cornwall.

Lea Wood. Cylinder top and top nozzles. The chest contains only the admission and equilibrium valves; the hand governor valve is in the steam pipe.

hollow and weighted with scrap. Parallel motion is fitted to both ends of the beam, as the pump rod is short.The beam itself is about 33 ft long and 30 ft between centres. A centre rib is cast in each beam plate and the plates are fixed close together with the parallel motion loops outside. Cornish engineers had early dispensed with the centre rib and they fitted their parallel motion loops inside the beam plates.

The cylinder is without a steam jacket and of the top nozzles only the steam and equilibrium valves are enclosed in a chest, the hand governor valve being fitted into the steam pipe before entering the chest. Below floor level and to one side of the cylinder is the condenser and the air pump is driven by the plug rod. Nearer to the beam centre a vertical rod from the beam drives the boiler feed pump also below floor. In Cornish practice these auxiliaries were usually 'outdoors' and in fact this engine has a set of holes in the outdoor end of the beam for the attachment of rods to drive the auxiliaries.

The original boilers worked at only 20 psi and appear to have stood outside. The present boilers are in a house carefully designed to match the engine house. They were specially built for stationary use, carrying numbers 43 and 44 and are not second-hand railway engine boilers. The boiler 'chimneys' are at the bottom of the smokeboxes dropping into the main flue to the chimney. Circular apertures closed by shutters in the boiler house rear wall opposite each smokebox allow access for the tube brush and for re-tubing. Standing on a substantial square base the octagonal chimney built in stone is 95 ft high. A cast-iron crown incorporates a venturi arrangement to improve the draught.

Mounted on the boiler house wall adjacent to the firing floor is a single cylinder boiler-feed pump with 'banjo' connecting rod. This draws from a boiler-feed tank built into the engine house. It is intended to bring other engines to this site for preservation and a small twin horizontal engine by George Mills of Radcliffe is already here. A twin cylinder horizontal Robey engine at a nearby refractory brickworks is also due to come here.

The Cromford Canal Society in conjunction with Derbyshire County Council has restored the engine, boilers and buildings to a high standard. Access is week-ends but obtain details from S.S.Stoker Esq, Winster, Matlock, Derbyshire.

LEICESTERSHIRE MUSEUM OF TECHNOLOGY, Abbey Pumping Station, Corporation Road, Leicester

WOOLF COMPOUND SEWAGE WORKS PUMPING ENGINES (4)
Gimson & Co, Leicester 1891, 30 in × 69¼ in (HP), 48 in × 96 in (LP), internal cut-off piston valves (hand adjusted), twin plate steel beam 12 rpm, 200 hp, 80 psi. Two plunger sewage pumps.

This pumping station was built to pump sewage from the outfall to a sewage farm located on high ground north of the city. The station still deals with storm water by automatic electric pumps, but the engines became redundant in 1965 when a new works was completed at Wanlip. Fortunately the engines were retained and now form part of the Leicestershire Museum of Technology.

The engines are contained in one house and

Abbey Pumping Station No 3. The beam is built up from two steel plates.

are house-built with cast-iron columns under the beam trunnions. While four engines in one house is not unique there were not many installations with this feature and this is the only place open to the general public. The cylinders are steam jacketted and have wood strip lagging secured by polished brass bands. The valve gear is under the driving floor and comprises eccentrics mounted on a layshaft which is driven by bevel gears from the crankshaft. Exhaust steam passed to a jet condenser below the floor. Injection water was drawn from the River Soar. The sewage pumps are located in a basement below the condensers. On each engine one pump is below the HP cylinder and driven by an extension of the HP piston tail rod. The other pump is 'outdoors' of the beam fulcrum and driven by rods coupled to the beam by parallel motion. The condenser air pump is driven by a rod from the indoor end of the beam also guided by parallel motion. There are no other auxiliary pumps, boiler feed water was supplied by separate steam driven pumps.

Steam was supplied by eight Lancashire boilers made by Gimson & Co, but these were entirely replaced in 1925 by new Lancashire boilers made by John Thompson of Wolverhampton. These had corrugated flues,

Abbey Pumping Station No 3. The engines are arranged in two pairs which enables one to stand back and appreciate their size. Note the decorated cast iron columns. ▼

Abbey Pumping Station No 3. These engines are the largest Woolf compounds surviving in the United Kingdom.

dished ends and were 7 ft diameter by 28 ft long. They were fitted with Proctor's mechanical stokers. The boiler installation was very plain without such refinements as economisers or superheaters, although the Thompson boilers were fitted with Hotchkiss circulators. Seven of the boilers were scrapped after closure of the station and the remaining boiler is not yet operative. No 3 engine was refurbished in 1974 and a second-hand vertical Cochran boiler was installed to run the engine without load. This boiler has an oil burner and automatic controls.

A variety of other engines are exhibited in the former boiler house.

A-FRAME TANK BED SINGLE-BEAM ENGINE
Unknown date and make.

This engine, from an Oxford brewery, is one of the varieties of tank-bed engine, another variation having six columns. The four-spoke flywheel is distinctive and its light construction and large diameter is typical of these old engines. Drive to the brewery machinery was through bevel gearing and a vertical shaft, part of which has been preserved with the engine. As received the cylinder bore was worn oval and restoration of the engine necessitated a rebore. Re-erection of the engine revealed a marked misalignment of the cylinder and the reason for the wear was now apparent. The alignment has now been corrected and the engine is now run regularly under steam.

SINGLE CYLINDER HORIZONTAL ENGINE
Buxton & Thornley, Burton-on-Trent.

The makers of this engine were principally brewery engineers, but supplied many small engines and pumps to the area around Burton-on-Trent. This engine is typical and was originally fitted with fixed cut-off Meyer expansion valves. The rider valve has at some time been removed, possibly to enable more power to be extracted from the engine at the cost of economy.

Leicestershire Museum of Technology. Tank-bed beam engines were often made in A-frame configuration. Note the decoration on columns and bed.

Leicestershire Museum of Technology.
Worthington - Simpson 'Duplex' direct acting pump. Note the arrangement of the linkage taking motion from one piston rod to the slide valve on the other side.

HORIZONTAL DIRECT-ACTING DUPLEX BOILER FEED PUMP
Worthington-Simpson Ltd, Newark-on-Trent

Patented by Henry Worthington in the USA manufacture was taken up under licence by James Simpson in the UK and eventually the two firms combined to form a British company. Like many highly successful inventions the duplex pump is simplicity in itself. There is no connection between the piston rods of each side, but the piston rod of one side operates the slide valve of the other and by this means each side of the pump makes its stroke alternately. Similar pumps were made by other manufacturers, but the Worthington-Simpson output was overwhelming. As with the makers of another kind of pump the duplex boiler feed pump was often called 'Worthington' whether it was of that manufacture or otherwise. The pump was made in much larger sizes with tandem-compound and triple-expansion cylinders, in which form it achieved considerable popularity as a waterworks pump.

SINGLE-STAGE IMPULSE TURBINE
Greenwood & Batley, Leeds.

The use of impulse turbines coupled to centrifugal pumps was widespread in hospitals for circulation of hot water for heating and domestic supplies. Running at about 1,450 rpm the turbine was very inefficient at this speed. Similar turbines driving generators would run at 30,000 rpm with a reduction gearbox drive to the generator. However the low efficiency

when used in the hospital pumping application was of no account for the exhaust steam was passed directly to calorifiers (steam-to-water tubular heat exchangers) to provide heating and hot water services.

DISHED-END LANCASHIRE BOILER
John Thompson & Co Ltd, Wolverhampton, 1926, 7 ft × 28 ft, 80 psi.

The dished-end Lancashire boiler was a characteristic product of John Thompson. The dished ends gave great strength and rigidity so much so that the furnace tubes were made corrugated like a concertina to take up expansion and contraction. This boiler is the sole survivor of a range of eight installed to supply steam to the beam pumping engines. These boilers had replaced boilers made and installed by Gimson in 1891.

COCHRAN VERTICAL SMOKE-TUBE BOILER
Cochran & Co Ltd, Annan, 1925, 85 psi

The traditional vertical boiler is inefficient, of low steam-raising capacity and has the poor feature that the uptake, which is subject to intense heat, is dry between the water line and the crown of the boiler. The Cochran boiler, first made in 1877, used a special arrangement of horizontal smoke tubes in a vertical shell to keep all the heated surfaces below the water line. The first design of boiler had a flat crown but this was quickly changed to a hemispherical crown, or a dished crown on the smaller boilers. This feature, together with the hemispherical firebox, gave great strength and durability. An efficiency well in excess of 70 per cent could be achieved. Twenty-four sizes of boiler were made varying in output from 300 to 10,800 lb of water evaporated per hour when coal fired. Oil fired versions were also available and these were often used as auxiliary or 'donkey' boilers on board ship. The boiler here is a Size No 14, rated at 2,400 lb per hour and served as a coal fired boiler until 1974 at Vestry Street Baths in Leicester. It was then removed to the museum and in 1976 was fitted with a Typhoon oil burner and fully automatic water level and pressure controls. The boiler is in regular service providing steam for heating buildings on the museum site when not running one of the beam engines.

The museum is open daily, except Christmas holidays and steam week-ends are held about four times per year.

MARKFIELD ROAD SEWAGE PUMPING STATION, Tottenham, London

WOOLF COMPOUND EIGHT-COLUMN PUMPING ENGINE
Wood Bros, Sowerby Bridge, 1886, 21 in × 52 in (HP), 36 in × 72 in (LP), piston valves (semi-rotating cut-off on HP). Two ram pumps 36 in × 52 in 3.7 mgp, 18 rpm, 80 psi.

A very large example of a self-contained beam engine completely independent of its house. The sewage pumps as usual are below floor level and are placed one on either side of the beam fulcrum centre line. One pump is driven by an extension of the HP tail rod while the other is directly coupled by rod to the beam. The piston valves with semi-rotating cut-off add a touch of what was contemporary northern mill engine practice.

Access is by application to the Attendant in the adjacent public park.

PINCHBECK PUMPING STATION, Spalding Marsh, Lincs

A-FRAME ENGINE & SCOOP WHEEL
Maker unknown, 1833, 25 in × 54 in. piston valve, flywheel 19 ft 6 in diameter. Cast iron single plate beam, 30 rpm. Scoop wheel 24 ft diameter, 2 ft 2 in wide, forty ladles, 6¾ rpm. Galloway boiler 1898, 6 ft × 18 ft, 80 psi.

A-frame beam engines were much used for fen drainage. The power required was usually fairly low which meant that A-frame construction was adequate. Also all parts of the engine were tied to a bedplate which meant a lesser chance of misalignment on foundations liable to subsidence.

Pinchbeck was the last beam engine and scoop wheel to work in the fens, ceasing work in 1952 when the boiler needed extensive repairs. Originally built with slide valves the piston valve was fitted by Worthington-Simpson to improve efficiency. The valve gear is the original gab type with an eccentric on the crankshaft and lattice eccentric tod. Condenser, air pump and boiler feed pump are below floor, the pumps being operated by rods from the beam. The air pump rod is guided by parallel motion. Drive to the scoop wheel is by spur wheel and pinion, the gear wheel for the scoop wheel being fitted to the wheel shaft. Often scoop wheels had an internal gear ring.

Access to the engine house is at all reasonable times.

Pinchbeck. The A-frame type of beam engine was much used in fen drainage. Note the cast iron cruciform connecting rod and the wrought iron guard rails.

Pinchbeck. Cylinder top. Note the cast iron packing platform fitted around the cylinder and the cylindrical steam chest for the piston valve, which replaced the original slide valve.

MIDDLETON INCLINE,
Middleton by Wirksworth, Derbys

TWIN BEAM WINDING ENGINE
The Butterley Company, c1825, 23 in × 64 in, gab valve gear, slide valves, 30 rpm. Two Cornish boilers 5 psi, 1860.

Many of the early railways were built over hilly ground to connect canals. The Cromford & High Peak Railway connected the Cromford Canal at Cromford with the Peak Forest Canal at Whaley Bridge. These lines were built in similar manner to canals with level stretches on which the wagons were horse hauled, interspersed with nine steep sections corresponding to flights of locks. On the inclines stationary engines were installed for haulage. The Middleton Incline engine is the last of the Cromford & High Peak Railway winding engines to survive and worked from about 1825 to 1963. The Middleton Incline was 800 yd long on a gradient of 1 in 8¼ with double track. The engine was geared to a sheave wheel around which the haulage rope passed and the descending load assisted the engine.

The engine is house-built with the entablature additionally supported under the beam trunnions by cast iron columns. The beams are twin plate cast iron and the connecting rods are also of cast iron of cruciform cross-section. The valve gear is driven by loose eccentrics on the crankshaft and the valves need to be worked by hand until the engine is going in the right direction. The eccentric rods are then dropped over a pin on the valve rods and the valve gear takes over. Exhaust steam passed to a condenser under the floor; the air pump discharged to a cooling pond, which is now filled in.

The boilers are of a very old pattern with rivetted joints in the furnace tubes, instead of the later Adamson joints which kept the rivet heads out of the flame path. They were served by a prominent square chimney which still exists but is unused, as are the boilers.

When the engine ceased work it was designated an Ancient Monument. Restoration was carried out by the Derbyshire Archaeological Society in conjunction with Derbyshire County Council. The engine is open to the public every Sunday; access at other times is by prior arrangement. The engine is run on low air pressure on the first Sunday in every month. Although the winding ropes and the

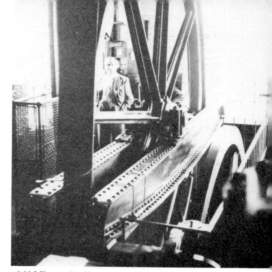

Middleton Incline. Most of the flywheel is below ▲ *floor level and the top is seen in this view. The large wheel carried on joists is an idler carrying the haulage rope. The haulage wheel is below in a pit, gear driven from the crankshaft.*

Middleton Incline. The beam loft is a narrow walkway around the perimeter of the engine house, but now a hand rail has been fitted.

rails on the incline have been removed it is hoped to reconstruct the winding arrangements at the top of the incline in the near future.

PAPPLEWICK PUMPING STATION
Nottinghamshire

SINGLE BEAM WATERWORKS PUMPING
ENGINES (2)
James Watt & Co, Soho Works, Birmingham,
1884, 46 in × 7 ft 6 in. Cornish double beat
valves, twin plate cast iron beam, flywheel 20 ft
diameter. Bucket-type well pump 20 in × 7 ft
6 in, double acting force pump 27½ in × 3 ft 9 in.
140 hp, 1½ mgd, 11½ rpm. Six Galloway boilers 7 ft × 28 ft 7 in, 55 psi, made 1883.

Papplewick is some 8 miles north of Nottingham in the Sherwood Forest and lies on the
heavily water bearing Bunter Sandstone. During the nineteenth century Nottingham
Waterworks sunk several wells into the sandstone and erected a number of pumping
stations to supply Nottingham with pure water.
The architecture of these stations was highly
ornate. Although Papplewick was not the most
ornate externally the internal decorations and
stained glass windows left no doubt that here
was a 'Temple to the God of Steam'.

The chief engineer at Nottingham, Mr Ogle
Tarbotton, was determined that the engines
should be as reliable as possible and for this
reason single cylinder engines were chosen.
The engines are house built, with columns
under the beam trunnions decorated with
birds, fishes and flowers in brass tracery.
Thermal insulation of cylinders and steam
pipework within the engine house is by
polished wood strips secured by brass bands.
Inlet and exhaust valves are cam operated, the
camshaft being fixed at about mid-cylinder
height and driven by an inclined shaft and an
under floor horizontal shaft by bevel gearing
from the crankshaft. Exhaust is to a jet con-

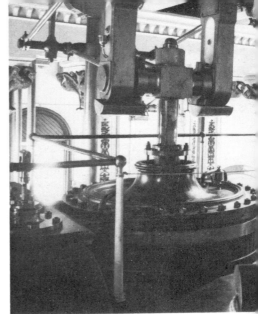

Papplewick. The packing floor. As the name
implies this gives access to the cylinder tops for
packing the piston rod glands. Note the scroll
work on the column heads in the background.

Papplewick. The beam chamber. Note the centre
ribs cast in the beam plates.

Papplewick. A 'Cameron' type single cylinder pump made by Thomas Matthews, Manchester. It is not used for pumping, but drives workshop machinery by belt.

Papplewick. Six Galloway boilers, possibly the largest range of these boilers now surviving.

denser below floor. Air pump and boiler feed pump are also below the floor, driven by rods connected to the 'outdoor' end of the beam. Overspeed control is by Watt-type governor.

The well is 18 ft × 7 ft cross section and 202 ft deep. A pilot well also 202 ft deep is connected to the main well by a heading. Water is induced to flow into the well by a series of headings and boreholes. The well pump is driven by rod and spears attached to the nose of the beam. The connecting rod is fitted just indoors of the pump rods and turns a crank of 3 ft 3 in throw. Below the floor and driven from the indoor end of the beam is the force pump which delivered water to Ramsdale reservoir. A large ornamental cooling pond in the grounds of the pumping station supplies the needs of the condenser.

The six Galloway patent boilers probably represent the largest single installation of these boilers surviving in this country. Two boilers are at present workable. Four boilers were fitted with forced draught furnaces at some time but this equipment was later removed although the furnace doors remain. The other two boilers are in their original state and retain the distinctive Galloway fire doors with circular air vents and very heavy construction. An ornamental square section chimney serves the boilers. In the workshop a single cylinder 'Cameron' type pump made by Thomas Matthews of Manchester has been cunningly adapted to drive the machinery by fitting a belt pulley alongside the flywheel.

Access to the pumping station is on Sunday afternoons April to October, and full steam week-ends are held about nine times per year. Details from the Custodian, Papplewick Pumping Station, Longdale Lane, Ravenshead, Notts, NG15 9AJ.

43

PRESTONGRANGE MINING MUSEUM,
Prestonpans, East Lothian

CORNISH PUMPING ENGINE
Harvey & Co, Hayle, Cornwall, 1874, 70 in ×
12/10 ft. Bottom lift (17 in pump) at 806 ft
level, middle lift (28 in pump) at 576 ft level,
top lift (28 in pump) at 318 ft level. Twin-plate
cast-iron beam 33 ft long × 6 ft 4 in deep at
centre, single plug rod, single cataract,
650 gpm, 3½ spm.

Prestongrange Colliery was worked to a great
extent under the Firth of Forth and reliable
drainage was essential. This engine was erected
here in 1874 having been brought by sea from
Cornwall. Extension of the workings at
Prestongrange necessitated larger pumps being installed in 1905. The new pumps were
made by Messrs Andrew Barclay of Kilmarnock. To cope with the increased load king
posts and bridles were fitted to the beam.
Large bolt holes were drilled in the beam by
a boring bar driven by a steam engine. After
fitting, the bridles were carefully tightened,
the deflection of the beam being measured to
avoid over-stressing.

The steam cylinder is the original and has no
steam case. In 1916 the piston rod broke on the
steam stroke and the piston smashed through

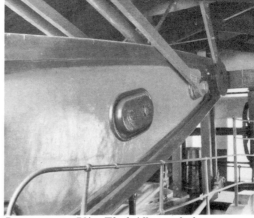

*Prestongrange 70in. The bridles on the beam are
bolted directly to the beam plates.*

the cylinder bottom also cracking the cylinder
wall. A new cylinder bottom was made and the
cylinder repaired by caulking the cracks with
red lead and bolting clamps around the
cylinder. In 1938 the piston rod broke again,

*Prestongrange 70in. The separate valve nozzles
and the push-up arrangement of the valve levers
are seen in this view of the cylinder top. Note the
piston rod gland in two halves – no doubt a local
modification to simplify maintenance.*

smashing the cylinder bottom and further damaging the cylinder wall. A new bottom was again made and to repair the cylinder wall the clamping rings were removed to expose the cracks. Dovetailed grooves were cut, soft copper strips driven in and the whole clamped up again. This tough old engine then continued to work until 1954 when it was retired but fortunately left in position. When the colliery closed in 1964 the engine was designated an ancient monument. By the time restoration could start it was in a sorry state with timber floors and staircases ripped out. Although the engine cannot now be worked restoration has been of a high order.

The Prestongrange engine has a number of what are now unique features. The steam and equilibrium valves are in separate nozzles bolted to the cylinder and separate ports are provided for inlet and equilibrium steam. The valve levers are also pushed up to lift the valve stems to open the valves. The steam arbor is transposed from the normal position and is the bottom one of the three arbors instead of the top as was more usual practice. The two perpendicular pipes are of different sizes and only one in fact carries equilibrium steam; the other conveys live steam upwards to the inlet valve.

Recent research has revealed that the Prestongrange engine although usually attributed to Harvey & Co is in fact a Harvey rebuild of an engine built by J. E. Mare & Co of Plymouth Foundry in 1853. Designed by Hocking & Loam, the Redruth consulting engineers it was made as an equal beam 12 ft stroke engine, one of several designed by Cornish engineers and built by a number of foundries around that time. This Devon-built engine was made for a Devon mine — Exmouth & Adams United at Christow on the eastern edge of Dartmoor. It was sold in 1862 to Old Wheal Neptune, Perranuthnoe in Cornwall and then sold again in 1869 to Great Western Mines at nearby Marazion. Great Western closed in 1873 and Harvey & Co bought the engine — in poor condition as it turned out. Harvey's cast a new beam and probably fitted a new piston rod. Others, now unknown, carried out further repairs before the engine was despatched to Prestongrange in the summer of 1874.

The museum section is housed in the former power house and is devoted to mining

Prestongrange. Howden high speed compound engine. Note the large belt driven Pickering governor – not a usual feature of high speed engines.

machinery, including several stationary steam engines. Additionally a winding engine is being erected adjacent to one of the colliery shafts.

> INVERTED VERTICAL COMPOUND HIGH SPEED ENCLOSED FAN ENGINE FROM NEWCRAIGHALL COLLIERY

Built by Howden of Glasgow this engine is a rare survivor of the high speed engine as applied to a mine ventilating fan. Unfortunately the fan has not survived, but would be of the forward-curved blade pattern. This type ran at a much higher speed than the backward-curved blade fan and could be directly coupled to a high-speed steam engine.

> TWIN CYLINDER HORIZONTAL HAULAGE ENGINE
> Inglis of Airdrie, slide valves, Stephenson's link motion.

A very elegant little engine, which in its

working location was geared to a winding drum, now missing. Unusually there is a flywheel, offset from the centre line of the engine. In the centre position is the pinion which engaged with the winding drum. Most haulage engines of the twin cylinder type did not possess a flywheel as with cranks at 90° one was not necessary.

SINGLE CYLINDER DIRECT ACTING PUMP
Joseph Evans, Wolverhampton.

Known as the 'Cornish' pattern pump by the makers, this horizontal pump is double acting. The water barrel has two single acting rams operating back to back, the motion of the ram furthest from the steam cylinder being obtained by side rods and crosshead. When used underground these pumps usually operated on compressed air.

VERTICAL DIRECT ACTING SINGLE
CYLINDER PUMP, G. & J. Weir, Cathcart.

This very large example of the Weir boiler feed pump was once a common sight in colliery 'fireholes'. Such a pump could supply a whole range of Lancashire boilers. They were so common that even when similar pumps of other makes were installed they were often collectively called 'Weir Pumps'.

Prestongrange. Evans's horizontal direct acting pump – 'The Cornish'. Its slim lines and simplicity made it ideal for use underground.

TWIN CYLINDER HORIZONTAL WINDING
ENGINE FROM NEWCRAIGHALL COLLIERY.
Grant, Ritchie & Co, Kilmarnock, 1909, 24 in × 60 in, slide valves, parallel drum.

A very plain engine with no refinements or concessions to economy, but simple and robust. Still in course of re-erection.

The museum is open every Sunday 9-30a.m. to 4-30p.m. from the beginning of April to the end of September. Visits at other times are by arrangement. Details from David Spence, 24 Woodlands Grove, Edinburgh 15.

RYHOPE PUMPING STATION, Co Durham

WOOLF COMPOUND WATERWORKS PUMPING
ENGINES (2)
R. & W. Hawthorn, Newcastle-on-Tyne, 1868, 27½ in × 64 in (HP), 45 in × 96 in (LP). Cornish valves, twin plate cast-iron beam, 33 ft centres, flywheel 24 ft diameter. Bucket lift pumps 10 ft 8 in stroke, 1 mgd against 243 ft head, 10 rpm. Three Lancashire boilers by W. & J. Galloway, Manchester, 1908, superheaters, 35 psi.

Well sinking at Ryhope commenced about 1865 into heavily water bearing limestone. The main well is 15 ft diameter by 257 ft deep with a borehole sunk below. An elliptical staple well 14 ft × 10 ft and 140 ft deep was sunk adjacent. Each engine drove a bucket pump in the main well delivering into the staple well from which a second bucket pump delivered to a reservoir at the surface. The pumprods are connected to the extremities of the beam: the main pump at the flywheel end and the staple well pump at the cylinder end. The points of attachment for connecting rod and piston rods are set in from the ends of the beam. Piston rods and pump rods are guided by Watt parallel motion. Pump rods are wrought iron for the first length with timber 'spears' below. The engines are house-built with cast iron columns under the entablature at the beam trunnions.

Steam and exhaust valves are operated by lifting handles and cam gear from an under-floor layshaft bevel gear driven from the crankshaft. Exhaust steam passes to a condenser under the floor outdoors of the beam centre. Condensate is removed by the air pump into the hotwell from which the boiler feed pump supplies the boilers' or pumps' surplus condensate into the cooling pond outside. Each engine has its own cooling pond. Indoors of the beam centre, also below floor level, is the jack-head pump whose function is to supply injection water from the cooling pond to the condenser. All the auxiliary pumps are driven by rods from the beam.

Steam was originally supplied by six Cornish boilers which were worn out by 1908. The present boilers are plain Lancashire type and not Galloway's patent type. The superheaters were fitted in 1931 to improve efficiency. In the boiler house is the stand-by boiler feed pump, a twin cylinder 'Cameron' type made by Evans of Wolverhampton.

Ryhope. Engine house with boiler house and ▲ *chimney beyond.*

Auxiliary engines are provided for powering winches to lift the spears and pumps from the wells. One engine is located under the engine house steps. The other, resides on the beam floor.

The whole of the limestone area in Durham eventually became grossly over pumped resulting in the ingress of sea water into the strata. When new upland sources became available Ryhope was closed, the last engine stopping on 1 July 1967. After closure a Trust was formed to preserve the entire works and with the help of the Water Company this has been achieved. The station is open at weekends Easter to September and running weekends are held from time to time during this period. Details from Ryhope Engines Trust, Ryhope Pumping Station, Ryhope, Sunderland, Tyne & Wear.

Ryhope. The beam chamber. ▲

Ryhope. View along the packing platform showing cylinder tops and top nozzles. ▼

STRETHAM PUMPING STATION, Ely, Cambs

Stretham. Beam chamber from the connecting rod end. Note the neat drip tray at the top of the connecting rod.

Stretham. Looking down from the driving floor.

BEAM ENGINE & SCOOP WHEEL
Butterley Co, 1831, rebuilt by Petrie & Co, Rochdale, 1909, 39 in × 8 ft. Internal cut-off piston valve, cast-iron twin plate beam, 24 ft 8½ in centres, flywheel 24 ft diameter, 16 rpm. Scoop wheel 37 ft 2 in diameter × 2 ft 5 in wide, forty-eight ladles, 4 rpm, 26,800 gpm. Three Lancashire boilers 7 ft × 22 ft 9 in, 8 psi by Butterley Co, 1871 (2) and 1878(1).

Scoop wheels were first used in conjunction with windmills for fen drainage. Later they were used with steam engines until ousted by centrifugal pumps. Very simply a scoop wheel is a water wheel in reverse, literally paddling up water from a low level to a higher level. It was suitable for large quantities and low lifts hence its widespread use in the fens.

The Stretham engine was built for steam at 4 psi supplied until 1871 by 'waggon top' boilers. Exhaust was to a condenser below the floor. Originally there was no boiler feed pump, as the steam pressure was low enough to allow gravity feeding of the boilers from a 'jack head' cistern. Control was by a float and chain mechanism in the boiler which operated a valve in the feed pipe. A brass pointer connected to this mechanism indicated the boiler water

Stretham. Lancashire boilers presenting an unusual appearance with ashpit doors and single inclined water gauge.

level. This old system, although still in position on two boilers, was replaced by an engine-driven feed pump in 1888 when boiler pressure was raised to 8 psi. Proper water gauges were fitted to the boilers at this time.

As built the engine had split slide valves which by later standards were inadequate for the steam flow. The piston valve fitted by Petrie, with hand adjusted cut-off, contributed a marked increase in efficiency. The internal cut-off valve was driven by linkage from the beam. Little else was changed on the engine which retained its cruciform connecting rod and Watt type throttle governor. Due to shrinkage of the soil as the fen was drained it was necessary to increase the size of the scoop wheel in 1850. Because of the greater lift the ladles were reduced in width from 3 feet to 2 ft 5 in. Further shrinkage necessitated the complete rebuilding of the wheel to its present size in 1896.

The engine ceased regular work in 1925 when a Mirlees diesel engine and centrifugal pump was installed. It was retained as a standby for a number of years and last ran in 1941. The Stretham Engine Trust now cares for the engine. Access is at all reasonable times.

Stretham. Cylinder top. Note the internal cut-off gear driven by linkage from the beam.

WASHINGTON 'F' PIT,
Washington, Tyne & Wear

> HORIZONTAL TWIN CYLINDER COLLIERY WINDING ENGINE.
> Grange Iron Company, Durham, 1888, 30 in × 54 in.

This engine has been preserved in situ by Washington Development Corporation and is one of very few preserved colliery winding engines. The engine worked until 1968 although as preserved it is not operational.

2 ENGINES IN MUSEUMS (PUBLIC & PRIVATE) Or on Public Display

ABBOT'S HALL MUSEUM,
Stowmarket, Suffolk

> SINGLE CYLINDER HORIZONTAL ENGINE
> Whitmore & Binyon, Wickham Market.

An example of an engine built locally for a local need. Many small engineering firms used to supply a complete service to local industry, including the building of steam engines. These were usually in the lower power ranges. Local engineering sometimes also extended to the supply of boilers.

Access to the engine is 1 April to 31 October, 2.00-5.00p.m.

ASTON, Birmingham

> SINGLE BEAM NON-ROTATIVE BLOWING
> ENGINE FROM M. & W. GRAZEBROOK LTD
> Possibly Boulton & Watt , Soho Works,
> Birmingham, c1817, 48 in × 8 ft stroke, beam
> 27 ft centres, blowing cylinder or 'tub' 7 ft ×
> 8 ft stroke.

This historic engine is exhibited on a roundabout at the southern end of the A38(M) Aston Expressway. Provision is made for it to be operated electrically. The engine is of the first generation of ironworks blowing engines, being non-rotative. Later types of blowing engine were rotative and this development is seen in the engines preserved at Blist's Hill, Ironbridge Gorge Museum.

BANKFIELD MUSEUM,
Boothtown Road, Halifax, Yorks

> SINGLE CYLINDER HORIZONTAL MILL
> ENGINE
> FROM ALMA TANNERY, PUDSEY, YORKS
> Newton, Bean & Mitchell Ltd, Bradford,
> 1926, 14 in × 24 in, flywheel 10 ft diameter
> 120 hp, 120 rpm.

Newton, Bean & Mitchell built mill engines until the 1930s, but this moderately-powered engine is now the sole survivor of their conventional products in the UK. A uniflow built in 1937 still powers a sawmill in New Zealand and

another uniflow exists in a derelict state in Yorkshire. This engine went second-hand to the tannery in 1948, and saw service until 1978 when the works closed. The engine was removed in 1979 for restoration.

The Bankfield Museum is operated by the Metropolitan Borough of Calderdale, Museums & Art Galleries Service, Clay House, Halifax, from whom details should be obtained.

BASS MUSEUM,
Horninglow Street, Burton-on-Trent

> TANDEM COMPOUND HORIZONTAL MILL
> ENGINE
> FROM BASS CHARRINGTON, SLEAFORD
> Robey & Co, Lincoln, 1904, No 23856, 14 in
> (HP), 22½ in (LP) × 30 in stroke. Hartnell
> expansion slide valves HP, simple slide valve
> LP, Hartnell type governor, girder bed, trunk
> crosshead guides, disc crank, flywheel 13 ft
> diameter grooved for eight ropes, jet condenser
> behind LP cylinder, LP tail rod drive to air
> pump, 70 rpm, 200 hp approx.

One of two 'mirror image' sister engines supplied to Sleaford Maltings. The other engine No 23857 also survives in the care of Dr Francis at Forncett St Mary. The engine epitomises eastern England builder's practice and with governor controlled expansion slide valves combines simplicity with a high degree of efficiency. The layout of the engine keeps everything above floor making for simple installation and maintenance. The engine is in working order and is demonstrated from time to time usually Wednesday afternoons.

Access to the museum is on weekdays.

Bass Museum. Robey tandem compound engine No 23856, with jet condenser behind the LP cylinder and air pump driven by the LP tail rod. This is an all above floor layout; convenient but making a long engine. ▶

BIGGAR GASWORKS, Lanarkshire
SCOTTISH DEVELOPMENT DEPARTMENT/
ROYAL SCOTTISH MUSEUM

SINGLE CYLINDER HORIZONTAL ENGINE &
GAS EXHAUSTER
George Waller & Sons, Stroud, 9in × 12in
(approx), slide valve, overhung cylinder,
double web crank, flywheel 4ft diameter,
direct coupled to gas exhauster.

Biggar Gasworks has been preserved by the
Scottish Development Department in conjunction with the Royal Scottish Museum. It is
a unique piece of preserved industrial archae-
ology, typical of a nineteenth-century small
town gasworks with its horizontal hand-
charged retorts. The works was started in 1839
by the Biggar Gas Light Company who ran the
works until Nationalisation in 1949. Much of
the present plant dates from 1914.

The engine was not originally installed here,
but was donated from Dunoon Gasworks by
the Scottish Gas Board. The exhauster provided a suction on the gas-making retorts to
induce flow and Waller made many of these
small exhauster sets with engine and exhauster
mounted upon a common bedplate. Heavy
construction ensured long and trouble free
service and the engines would run for months
without attention apart from lubrication. The
'wiper' lubricators meant that even the oil cups
could be replenished without stopping the
engine. A vertical boiler, which is part of the
former working installation, supplies steam for
the engine. In working days its function was to
steam heat the gasholder water seals in winter
to prevent freezing.

The gasworks is open to the public with the
engine in operation on the first Sunday of each
month June to September noon until 5.00p.m.
Access at other times, usually for organised
parties, is by application to Mr J. L. Wood,
Department of Technology, The Royal Scottish Museum, Chambers St, Edinburgh.

*Biggar Gasworks. Single cylinder engine by
Waller of Stroud. The exhauster is directly
driven from the crankshaft. A small engine, but of
strong construction.*

BIRMINGHAM MUSEUM OF SCIENCE & INDUSTRY, Newhall Street, Birmingham.
Although the Science Museum at South Kensington pioneered the preservation of large stationary engines, Birmingham was the first to present engines running under steam. The collection contains a number of important engines of types which cannot at present be seen elsewhere.

The museum is open every day except Christmas Day, Boxing Day and Good Friday.

TANDEM COMPOUND HORIZONTAL MILL ENGINE
Pollit & Wigzell, Sowerby Bridge, 1909, 7½ in (HP), 15 in (LP) × 24 in stroke, Corliss valves, Whitehead governor, flywheel 8 ft 6 in diameter, surface condenser, 110 hp.

Pollit & Wigzell were prolific builders of mill engines and had an excellent reputation for the quality of their products. Quite a number of their engines survive but this is the only one in a museum and is also the only one available for public inspection at the present time. This engine possesses a far greater number of 'gadgets' than a normal mill engine, as it was used in a heat engines laboratory; full facilities are provided for measuring the performance under widely varying conditions. What ap-

pears to be a second flywheel was for a band brake which could be adjusted to put precise, but varying, loads on the engine. The jet condenser was usually fitted to mill engines, but the surface condenser on this engine would enable the exact amount of condensate from the exhaust steam to be measured, as cooling is by heat exchanger and not direct injection.

UNIFLOW ENGINE
W. & J. Galloway, Manchester, 1924, 12½ in × 26 in, drop valves, 64 hp.

The Uniflow engine was successfully developed by Professor Stumpf of Berlin, and patented in 1908, although the uniflow principle had first been evolved by an American, Jacob Perkins, as early as 1827. Its concept is to carry out the whole of the expansion of the steam in one cylinder, admission being cut off very early in the piston stroke. As the final temperature of the steam at exhaust is low, the exhaust is made through a ring of ports around the cylinder bore central

Birmingham Science Museum. Apart from the surface condenser the Pollit & Wigzell tandem compound (foreground) is typical of the maker's mill engine practice, although there are extra fittings for laboratory work.

Birmingham Science Museum. The Uniflow engine by W. & J. Galloway representing the ultimate in reciprocating steam engine efficiency. This small engine has a belt pulley to transmit the drive and 'Morecambe' electric stop motion on the stop valve. Depressing one of a number of buttons in the factory would cause the valve to shut.

INVERTED VERTICAL CENTRAL VALVE HIGH SPEED ENCLOSED ENGINES (2)
Willans & Robinson, 1887, 10 in (HP), 14 in (LP) × 6 in stroke (sectioned). Willans & Robinson, 1906, 6½ in (HP), 12½ (LP) × 6 in stroke.

along its length, which keeps all parts of the cylinder at a uniform temperature. The exhaust steam is released by the piston uncovering the central ports near the end of its stroke. This design required a cylinder and piston much longer than usual and the cylinder was bored barrel shaped so that under running conditions, with the ends always hotter than the centre, the bore became parallel.

The uniflow engine therefore had inlet valves only, always of the 'drop' type with governor controlled cut-off. As most of the return stroke of the piston was made with the exhaust ports closed this gave a high compression which reduced condensation at inlet and also cushioned the heavy moving parts. The weight of the piston could be a problem and many engines had special lightweight pistons fitted. To assist in starting hand-operated compression-release valves were fitted. Usually all moving parts except the valve gear were enclosed. The efficiency of the uniflow engine was the highest ever obtained from reciprocating steam engines. Most of the leading engine builders made them, but few survive. This quite small example is the only one readily accessible for viewing and it is regularly demonstrated running under steam.

The Willans high speed engine was the subject of a patent taken out in the 1870s, and general introduction took place from the mid-1880s. The 1887 engine is thus an early production model. The Willans engine was highly novel in concept; it was enclosed and used splash lubrication, and was the first engine to run at sufficiently high speed (up to 500 rpm) to enable it to be direct coupled to a high output electrical generator of small size. Willans used single-acting cylinders to avoid reversal of stresses in the moving parts. It was not until about 1890 that the introduction of forced lubrication enabled the successful development of the double-acting high-speed engine to take place. Single, compound and triple-expansion engines were made with the cylinders stacked in tandem so that there was a complete engine on the one crank. High outputs were obtained by making two- and three-crank engines. A three-crank triple-expansion engine had three sets of tandem triple-expansion cylinders making nine cylinders in all.

The pistons of the Willans engine are fixed to a large hollow piston rod or trunk *inside* which are the piston valves. The trunk is coupled to a crosshead, connecting rod and crank, and the valve eccentric is forged solid with the crank pin so that the piston valves have a relative movement to the trunk to give admission and exhaust. To ensure non-reversal of stresses, the crosshead is guided in a cylinder and on the upstroke air is compressed in the top of the guiding cylinder by the crosshead to give a downward load on the crankpin. Governing of Willans engines was by throttle valve operated by a centrifugal governor mounted on the crankshaft.

SIX-COLUMN WOOLF COMPOUND BEAM ENGINE
Easton, Amos & Sons, London, 1864, 10 in × 25 in (HP), 17 in × 36 in (LP), slide valves, beam 9 ft 10 in centres, flywheel 14 ft 2 in diameter.

Six-column beam engines of quite large sizes, were popular both for pumping and driving machinery. All structural parts were tied to a bedplate which eliminated the need for a massively built engine house. This engine is one of the smaller ones but the general construction was similar for all sizes. The engine has been fully restored and is regularly run under steam.

SINGLE COLUMN BEAM ENGINE
John Fowler, Leeds, 1872, 6 in × 18 in, slide valve, beam 6 ft 0 in centres, flywheel 4 ft 3 in diameter.

The single column design was very much used for small beam engines. All parts were carried on a bedplate and the engine was self contained. Some engines were very small indeed, as is this one. Its maker is far better known as a

Birmingham Science Museum. A very workaday single column beam engine by John Fowler. Note the complete lack of embellishment and the extensive use of lathe work in manufacturing the parts.

Birmingham Science Museum. Interconnected beam engines of single column and A-frame design. The A-frame engine has a twin plate beam. Both engines were probably made in the Black Country.

builder of steam ploughing engines, traction engines and steam rollers

INTER-CONNECTED SINGLE BEAM ENGINES
Makers unknown, c1840, high pressure engine 18 in × 60 in, beam 15 ft 6 in centres, flywheel 13 ft diameter; low pressure engine 26 in × 30 in, beam 9 ft 10 in centres, flywheel 8 ft 8 in diameter.

These engines were used to assist a waterwheel and if the installation had been done today it would have been called a 'bodge-up'. The engines are totally different from each other and are inter-connected by gearing. The low-pressure engine runs at a higher speed than the high-pressure engine to give an adequate swept cylinder volume for the low-pressure steam. In actual cylinder volume there is little difference between the two engines. The arrangement could be described as a novel form of 'pusher compounding'.

SEMI-PORTABLE BEAM ENGINE
Maker unknown, c1830, 6 in × 24 in, beam 70 in between centres, flywheel 80 in diameter.

A small self-contained beam engine made with the intention of being fairly easily moved from one site to another. This engine can be displayed in motion by an electric motor drive.

GRASSHOPPER BEAM ENGINE
Robert Stephenson, Newcastle-upon-Tyne, 1823, 15 in × 36 in, beam 8 ft centres, flywheel missing.

INVERTED VERTICAL SINGLE CYLINDER ENCLOSED ENGINES & GENERATORS
Robey & Co, Lincoln, 4 in × 3 in stroke, 2 hp.
Sissons of Gloucester, 3 in × 2½ in stroke, 3 hp.

Many of these engines were built to provide electric lighting to small premises or for providing local lighting. The Robey engine has been fully restored and can be run under steam.

INVERTED VERTICAL HIGH SPEED ENCLOSED COMPOUND ENGINE
Belliss & Morcom, Birmingham, 1891.

This engine is one of the very first double-acting high-speed engines which were pioneered by Belliss & Morcom. The forced lubrication to the bearings prevented knocking and seizing at the high rotational speeds at which these engines ran.

Birmingham Science Museum. Belliss & Morcom compound high speed engine and DC generator. The basic design of the engine has not changed much to the present day, but modern generators are very different in appearance.

SINGLE CYLINDER HORIZONTAL ENGINE
Messrs Tangye, Birmingham, 1891, slide valve, 4½ in × 7 in, 'Colonial' type.

As the name implies, this particular type of engine was built with an eye on the overseas market. Its sturdy construction meant that it would withstand a great deal of use and abuse. The quest for simplicity and reducing wearable parts to a minimum has led to the ingenious use of an extended slide-valve spindle to drive the boiler feed pump. The engine has been restored to run on steam once again.

Birmingham Science Museum. Tangye 'Colonial' engine. A very basic design with boiler feed pump driven by an extension of the slide valve spindle. Speed control is by Pickering governor.

HORIZONTAL CROSS COMPOUND ENGINE
Robey & Co, Lincoln, 5 in (HP), 7 in (LP) × 9 in stroke. Maker's No 21425.

This small engine built at the beginning of the century is slightly mysterious. The flywheel forms the rotor of an electrical generator, but neither this nor the stator appears to have had electrical windings. Alongside the rotor is a four-groove rope pulley. A possibility is that the engine was made for exhibition and sales promotion purposes and with its small size could fairly readily be transported from place to place. It still runs regularly under steam.

HYPERCYCLOIDAL SINGLE CYLINDER VERTICAL ENGINE
Built to Matthew Murray's Patent of 1802, Cylinder 5 in × 9 in, flywheel 5 ft 6 in diameter.

This is an engine without a connecting rod, the reciprocating motion of the piston rod being converted to rotative motion by an ingenious system of gearing, involving some rather complex geometry.

Gearwheels with teeth projecting from the rim are familiar enough but gearwheels with teeth on the inside of the rim are less so. By rotating a system of gearwheels with inside and outside teeth not only on their own axes but also around each other as in a planetary system, the wheel centres and points on the rims can be made to trace some peculiar paths. Murray devised such a system whereby one point was in straight line reciprocating motion and another in pure rotary motion about an axis. This axis became the flywheel shaft and the reciprocating point the attachment for the piston rod. The design was academic rather than practical, but similar principles are in common use today inside the gearboxes of motor cars with automatic transmission.

Birmingham Science Museum. The Murray hypercycloidal engine is fascinating to watch in action. The design eliminates a connecting rod and reduces the height of the whole engine.

THE BLACK COUNTRY MUSEUM,
Dudley, West Midlands
This museum is of recent origin, and there are a number of engines in the collection. The engines are mainly small and generally little is known of their history. The museum is open daily but precise times should be checked before visiting. (Phone 021 557 9643)

SINGLE BEAM ENGINE
Maker unknown, c1830, 24 in × 5 ft approx.
SINGLE CYLINDER HORIZONTAL ENGINES
G Adlam & Co, Bristol c1860, 10 in × 30 in.
Tangye, Birmingham, c1890, 14hp.
WINDING & WINCH ENGINES
Winding engine: Stark, Torquay, c1855, single cylinder 8 in × 24 in.
Winch engine: maker and date unknown, twin cylinder, 6 in × 14 in.
INVERTED VERTICAL SINGLE CYLINDER ENGINE
Tangye, Birmingham, c1900, 6hp.
STEAM PUMPS
Various by Tangye of Birmingham and Joseph Evans, Wolverhampton.

IRONBRIDGE GORGE MUSEUM,
Blist's Hill, Coalbrookdale, Shropshire.
The Blist's Hill site occupies what was formerly an extensive ironworks and mining site and is part of an extensive scheme covering the whole of the Coalbrookdale area. The object of the scheme is to preserve the industrial scene as it was in the eighteenth and nineteenth centuries. Access is daily.

TWIN-BEAM BLAST FURNACE BLOWING ENGINE
Murdoch, Aitken & Co, Glasgow, 1851, 38¾ in × 7 ft 10 in stroke, Cornish valves, twin plate cast-iron beams, flywheel 20 ft 4 in diameter, 12-16 rpm, 42 psi. Air cylinders 78 in × 7 ft 10 in stroke, 4 psi, 12,500 cfm, 137 hp at 12 rpm.

Installed at the Priorslee Furnaces of The Lilleshall Company, this cross-coupled pair of engines named *David* and *Sampson* provided blast air until 1900. From then until 1952 they were held on stand-by.

The steam cylinders are placed at the crankshaft end of the beams and the valves are in Gothic style, with top and bottom nozzles

Blists Hill. Crankshaft end of blowing engine, showing flitched timber connecting rod with steam cylinders beyond.

connected by fluted perpendicular pipes. The valve gear is operated by cam and roller gear on a cross-shaft below the floor, driven through bevel gearing from the crankshaft. The crankshaft is located beyond the extremity of the beams and this necessitates the up-turned ends for the attachment of the connecting rods. The connecting rods are of timber flitched with iron plates. At the further ends of the beams are the blowing cylinders or 'tubs'. Suction and delivery of air is controlled by simple pressure operated non-return valves. The air piston rods are connected to the ends of the beams and like the steam piston rods are guided by parallel motion.

INVERTED VERTICAL BLOWING ENGINE
The Lilleshall Company, Priorslee Works, 1886

A large single cylinder engine with the air cylinder placed above and in tandem with the steam cylinder. The engine has been re-erected in the blowing engine house of the Blist's Hill ironworks (closed 1912) which formerly housed a similar engine.

SINGLE CYLINDER HORIZONTAL WINDING ENGINE
Maker and date unknown, slide valve (on top of cylinder), gab valve gear, geared winding drum, single rope.

This engine has been re-erected at one of the shafts of the Blist's Hill mine. Coal and fireclay were worked until 1940 and the shaft was 202 yd deep. The engine came from the nearby Milburgh mine and with the timber headgear and single rope pulley the installation is little different from when Blist's Hill mine was working. A short section of the shaft has been re-opened and demonstration winding is performed. The whole is very typical of the profusion of small mines which operated in Shropshire during the nineteenth century. Steam is supplied by a vertical boiler which is not out of keeping with Shropshire mining and is in great contrast to the ranks of Lancashire boilers found at the large collieries in the north of England.

BOLTON,Lancs. Bradshawgate

SINGLE CYLINDER INVERTED VERTICAL
MILL ENGINE FROM LOW BENTHAM SILK
MILL
Hick, Hargreaves, Bolton, 1886, 24 in × 30 in,
Corliss valves, 150 hp, 88 rpm.

Preserved in a glass house the engine is turned
slowly by an electric motor. Without being
particularly impressive, because of its small
size, it is a good solid engine.

BRADFORD INDUSTRIAL MUSEUM,
Moorside Road, Bradford
An extensive museum still in course of
development. Three single-cylinder horizontal
engines are on display and a McNaught-
compounded beam engine is under erection.
This last is one of only two survivors in Britain
and is the only one which is in anything
approaching a complete state.

SINGLE CYLINDER HORIZONTAL ENGINES:
FROM OAK LEE MILLS, BRADFORD
J. B. Clabour, Guiseley, 1885. Powered mech-
anic's shop.
FROM HEARL, HEATON & CO, LIVERSEDGE
J. B. Clabour, Guiseley, 1906, named *Rhoda*.
Powered mechanic's shop.
From JOHN WHITE & SONS' TANNERY,
BINGLEY
Carr, Foster, Bingley, c1900. Provided power
for the tannery machinery.

McNAUGHT COMPOUNDED BEAM ENGINE
FROM E. & A. MATHEWS, EASTBURN.
William Bracewell & Co, Burnley, 1867, re-
built 1900, 18 in × 24 in (HP), 24 in × 48 in (LP),
Corliss valves HP, slide valve LP, flywheel
14 ft diameter.

The McNaught system of compounding,
patented in 1845, became very popular for
engines in the northern textile industry. It
served as a means of converting low-pressure
single-beam engines to use high-pressure
steam. Also many new engines were built to
this arrangement. With the high-pressure cylinder placed on a line between the crank and
the beam pivot the additional stresses on the
beam occasioned by the higher power output
were kept to a minimum. Nevertheless frac-
tures in the vicinity of the beam trunnion were
not unknown.

BY-GONES MUSEUM, HOLKHAM HALL,
Wells-Next-The-Sea, Norfolk
Depicting all aspects of rural life in East
Anglia, the museum has a small collection of
steam engines. Access times vary according to
the time of year and should be checked before
visiting.

COMPOUND PORTABLE ENGINE
The Farmer's Foundry Co, Ryburgh, Norfolk,
1921, No 39, slide valves

Although mounted on wheels the portable
engine was primarily a stationary engine when
in use, not being self propelling. Movement
from site to site was by horse haulage, the
steerable fore-carriage being fitted with shafts.
A portable engine is a complete power unit
usually comprising a locomotive-type boiler
with the engine, single-cylinder or compound,
mounted on top. The exhaust is turned into the
chimney to provide an induced draught. Boiler
feed is usually by a crankshaft-driven pump,
but an injector has been substituted on this
engine. The portable engine was the first really
successful application of steam power to agri-
culture. Introduced in the 1830s the basic
design had settled to its present form by the
end of the 1850s. Most preserved portable
engines are in private hands and appear at
many traction engine rallies.

The museum has a number of small station-
ery engines as static exhibits and these include
the following

Single Cylinder Horizontal. George Waller &
Son, Stroud, slide valve, Pickering governor.
Single Cylinder Inverted Vertical. Tangye &
Co, Birmingham 1891, slide valve, 3 hp.
Single Cylinder Vertical Oscillating. Stevens,
c1850, a tiny engine with oscillating cylinder.
The steam engine in its most rudimentary
form.
Vertical Single Cylinder. A small engine of
unknown date and make.
Banjo Pump. A type of pump often known as
'Mumford'. This one was made by Lister &
Branch of Cambridge.

BRIDEWELL MUSEUM,
Bridewell Alley, St Andrew St, Norwich

SINGLE COLUMN BEAM ENGINE c1840. FROM BAGG'S BREWERY

A small single column beam engine with 'buttresses' at the base of the column. Also at the museum are two small single-cylinder oscillating engines.

Access is daily but it is advisable to check times from the Castle Museum, Norwich.

CHEDDLETON FLINT MILL MUSEUM,
Leek, Staffs

SINGLE CYLINDER HORIZONTAL ENGINE Robey & Co, Lincoln

This flint mill was always water powered by two impressive waterwheels which worked into the 1960s. The steam engine is a museum piece only and formerly provided power at Minton's pottery works in Stoke-on-Trent. The whole mill is well worth a visit and opening hours are usually Saturday and Sunday afternoons. Further information is available from the Tourist Information Office, 18 St Edward Street, Leek, Staffs.

DARTMOUTH, Devon, Royal Avenue Gardens

ATMOSPHERIC BEAM PUMPING ENGINE FROM HAWKESBURY JUNCTION, COVENTRY CANAL Maker and date unknown, rebuilt by Jonathan Woodhouse 1821, 22 in × 4 ft, wooden beam with arch head, single-beat drop-valves, plug-rod valve-gear, pickle-pot condenser.

Purchased second hand from Jonathan Woodhouse in 1821 by the Coventry Canal Co, the engine was erected at Hawkesbury Junction to supply water into the canal. The engine is a small one with an untrussed simple beam and was probably a Newcomen engine originally erected at a nearby colliery. As installed at Hawkesbury the engine was considerably modified from the original Newcomen design, principally by the addition of a pickle-pot condenser. The valve gear with its rack and pinion valve operating mechanism also probably dates from this time. The pickle-pot condenser, so called because of its shape, is a small chamber permanently connected to the cylinder. Instead of cooling water being injected direct into the cylinder it was now injected

Dartmouth. Open top cylinder, piston rod, chain and beam arch head of Newcomen atmospheric engine.

into the pickle-pot. This reduced the violent temperature fluctuations of the cylinder and saved steam. The system was applied to late Newcomen-type engines and many earlier ones were rebuilt to this system.

This engine's duty at Hawkesbury involved pumping from a shallow well and it was necessary to add a forcing weight to the pump rod to assist the engine on its outdoor stroke. It worked until 1913 and then stood disused until 1963, when members of the Newcomen Society erected it at Dartmouth to commemorate the inventor's birth there 300 years previously. As preserved the engine can be operated by a hydraulic system to pump from a well and demonstrate its operation. Access is daily.

DARWEN, Lancs.
Bolton Road, outside India Mill

CROSS COMPOUND HORIZONTAL MILL ENGINE
John & Edward Wood, Bolton, 1905, 19 in (HP), 32 in (LP) × 42 in stroke, Corliss valves, 15 ft diameter flywheel, rope drive, 450 hp, 75 rpm, 125 psi

This engine drove one of India Mill's weaving sheds until 1970 and is now preserved outside the main mill with its outstanding chimney. Typical in every way of John & Edward Wood's designs, all the Corliss valves are fitted below the cylinders. Trip gear is fitted to the valve gear on both cylinders, the HP gear being controlled by a Lumb's governor. The LP trip gear is hand adjusted. Exhaust was to a condenser below floor level with the air pump driven by a rocker arm from the LP crosshead.

DARWEN, Lancs. Blackburn Road

VERTICAL SINGLE CYLINDER MILL ENGINE FROM SUNNY BANK MILL, DARWEN, LANCS
Maker and date unknown, possibly Rishton Foundry in 1850s, slide valve.

Darwen. J. & E. Wood made neatness of outline a prime consideration as evidenced by this cross-compound engine. This was achieved by placing all the Corliss valves below the cylinders, albeit at a slight loss of efficiency.

Darwen. The method of display of the Sunny-bank Mill engine shows how the engine house formed part of the structure of the engine.

A good example of a house-built vertical engine, albeit of quite small size. It is exhibited alongside the Blackburn Road, and the method of presentation shows the engine house in section. The entablature supporting the crankshaft bearings is built into the engine house walls and the support given to the engine by the structure of the engine house is clearly indicated. The engine itself is plain and simple and cast iron predominates in its construction.

FORNCETT INDUSTRIAL STEAM MUSEUM
Forncett St Mary, Norwich

This museum with an extensive collection of stationary steam engines is a private venture started in the early 1970s by Dr Rowan Francis. By his strenuous efforts at raising finance, Dr Francis has made remarkable progress in a short space of time. The engines can be run under steam.

CROSS COMPOUND HYDRAULIC POWER ENGINE FROM TOWER BRIDGE, LONDON
Vickers, Armstrong, Newcastle-on-Tyne, 1941, No 1190SE, 18 in (HP), 30 in (LP) × 27 in stroke. Meyer expansion slide valve (HP), simple slide valve (LP), flywheel 9 ft diameter, 30 rpm, 80 psi. Two hydraulic force pumps coupled to piston tail rods.

Before electric power became widely available through the grid system hydraulic power using water at high pressure was employed to a far larger extent than is generally realised today. Major cities such as London, Manchester and Glasgow had many miles of high pressure water mains below the streets. Connections were taken into buildings to work lifts and other machinery and concert halls had their pipe organs blown by hydraulic power. Steam engines pumped water into hydraulic accumulators which stored the water under pressure for delivery into the mains. The accumulators were similar in principle to gas holders but held water instead of gas. When demand was heavy they sank down and were pumped up again when demand decreased. Tower Bridge had its own hydraulic power system working at 750 psi. This engine was installed to supplement two larger engines dating from 1894. Power was supplied through accumulators to eight 3-cylinder hydraulic engines which raised and lowered the bascules. There was plenty of stand-by capacity and only two hydraulic engines were required to operate the bridge at any one time.

Forncett St Mary. Armstrong-Whitworth cross-compound hydraulic power pumping engine from Tower Bridge. Pumping water up to 750 psi is quite a severe duty and the engine is of massive construction.

This engine and No 5055 were built to replace three beam engines at the Dover pumping station. No 5055 was commissioned in 1939 but because of the onset of World War II No 5056 lay in boxes at the works and was not put into service until 1954. It was the last steam pumping engine to be erected for waterworks service. The cylinders are supported by massive cast-iron columns at the back which also carry the surface condenser. The front cylinder supports are steel columns. The well pumps were driven by a three-throw crankshaft which formed an extension beyond the flywheel of the engine crankshaft. Below the engine bedplate were the three force pumps each driven by four rods from the crossheads. These rods also drove an oil pump for lubrication, an air compressor for maintaining air pressure in the delivery surge vessel and the condenser air pump. Normal operating speed was 22 rpm. A twin-cylinder inverted vertical barring engine was fitted, engaging with internal teeth on the flywheel rim.

Forncett St Mary. Worthington-Simpson triple expansion pumping engine from Dover being re-erected. The well-pump crankshaft, missing in the photograph, was coupled to the flange on the end of the crankshaft.

Forncett St Mary. Robey tandem compound engine, a superb example of Eastern England engineering. Governor controlled expansion valves on HP cylinder gave maximum possible economy with slide valves and very silent running.

TANDEM COMPOUND MILL ENGINE
FROM BASS CHARRINGTON, SLEAFORD,
LINCS
Robey & Co, Lincoln, 1904, No 23857, 14 in (HP), 22½ in (LP) × 30 in stroke. Hartnell expansion slide valve (HP), simple slide valve (LP), trunk crosshead guides, girder bed, flywheel grooved for eight ropes, 70 rpm, 200 hp, 150 psi.

A straightforward engine, typical of eastern England manufacturers, of which many were built and supplied all over the world. All parts are above floor level, making for simple installation. The condenser is behind the LP cylinder with air pump driven by the LP piston tail rod.

It is intended that the collection will eventually be open to the public on a regular basis. For the time being access is on open days and at other times by appointment.

Forncett St Mary. Jessop & Appleby single cylinder horizontal engine. The curved spoke flywheel, usual on old type gas and oil engines, is much less common on steam engines.

SINGLE CYLINDER INVERTED VERTICAL ENGINES (2)
FROM POPLAR GASWORKS, LONDON
Hunter & English, Bow, 1900, slide valves, 45 hp, 12 in × 16 in

SINGLE CYLINDER HORIZONTAL ENGINE
FROM SARSON'S MALT VINEGAR WORKS,
LONDON
Jessop & Appleby, Leicester, 1897, slide valve, 9 hp, 8 in × 14 in, flywheel 4 ft 6 in diameter.

SINGLE CYLINDER HORIZONTAL ENGINE
FROM REED'S PAPER MILLS
Ruston, Proctor & Co, Lincoln, slide valve, 7 hp.

TANDEM COMPOUND INVERTED VERTICAL
HIGH SPEED ENCLOSED ENGINES (2)
FROM LYON'S CORNER HOUSE, LONDON
Belliss & Morcom, Birmingham.

SINGLE CYLINDER INVERTED VERTICAL
HIGH SPEED ENCLOSED ENGINE
FROM WESTMINSTER HOSPITAL
W. H. Allen, Bedford.

BANJO PUMP (WALL MOUNTED)
FROM GUS, LEE & BOSWELL, GREAT
YARMOUTH
Boiler feed-water pump

INDUSTRIAL & SOCIAL HISTORY MUSEUM, Forth House, Kirkcaldy, Fife

A small museum with a considerable pictorial display of local industries, in particular linoleum manufacture, as the making of floor coverings is still a major industry in the town. The collection contains two locally-built engines, one of which is on display; the other, which has only recently ceased work, is scheduled for re-erection in the museum during 1981.

SINGLE CYLINDER A-FRAME VERTICAL ENGINE

Henry Balfour, Leven, c1862, 6 in × 12 in approx, slide valve.

A two-crank design with the steam cylinder coupled to one crank and a gas exhauster pump to the other, with the flywheel between. The exhauster pump is now missing but its crank remains.

Kirkcaldy Museum. In true Scottish style Douglas & Grant No 739 is a hefty engine, and the marine type big-end is another Scottish touch. Photographed at Glentana Mills whilst resting during 'piece time'.

SINGLE CYLINDER HORIZONTAL MILL ENGINE

Douglas & Grant, Kirkcaldy, No 739, 1923, 11 in × 30 in, Corliss valves, Grant's trip gear, Porter-type governor, girder bed, disc crank, trunk crosshead-guides, flywheel 8 ft diameter, diagonal boiler-feed pump driven from crankshaft, 'Morecambe' electric stop motion, 80 psi, 90 rpm, 60 hp.

This relatively small engine is far more important than would first appear. It was from the Dunnikier Foundry in Kirkcaldy, the works of Robert Douglas, that the first Corliss engine in the UK emerged in 1863. It seems likely that this was also the first Corliss engine to be built in Europe. Engine No 739 was one of the last engines to be built by Douglas & Grant and worked all its life at Glentana Mills, Alva, Clackmannanshire. Progressive electrification of the machinery in due course made the engine redundant and it ceased work in February 1979, the last surviving Douglas & Grant engine in Britain.

Access to the museum, which is adjacent to the railway station, is Monday to Friday afternoons only during May-September.

HAMILTON MUSEUM, Hamilton, Strathclyde

A small but impressive museum with an excellent motor car section. Two stationary engines are on static display.

SINGLE CYLINDER HORIZONTAL ENGINE
George Waller & Son, Stroud, 10 in × 12 in, Meyer expansion slide valve, overhung cylinder, double web crank.

Typical of Waller's robust engines for gas works use, this engine was used to drive an exhauster. A fascinating feature found on many gasworks engines is the wiper lubrication of big-end and crosshead. By this means these parts received a droplet of oil at each stroke from a static lubricator. This avoided stopping the engine to refill oil cups and often these engines would run continuously for months on end.

SINGLE CYLINDER INVERTED VERTICAL ENGINE
Marshall & Sons, Gainsborough, 4½ in × 8 in, slide valve, Pickering governor.

A typical Marshall product, almost mass produced and available 'off the shelf' to customers in need of a small power unit.

HIGHER MILL MUSEUM, Helmshore, Lancs

SIX-COLUMN TANK BED SINGLE BEAM ENGINE
FROM THOMAS REDFERN, FILE MAKERS, STOCKPORT
Peel, Williams & Peel, Soho Iron Works, Manchester, 1846, 12 in × 20 in, slide valve, 'gab' valve-gear, single-plate cast-iron beam, 5 ft 6 in centres, flywheel 9 ft diameter, 25 psi, 10 hp.

The tank-bed beam engine was self contained, except for the outer crankshaft bearing, and was popular for small powers. The tank bed contained the condenser, air pump, hot well, boiler-feed pump and condenser cooling water-pump. The whole unit could be installed in its place of work with a minimum of site preparation and construction work. This engine is a static exhibit only and did not work at this mill. The mill itself is a waterwheel-driven fulling mill dating from 1789, containing the original machinery which remained at work until 1967.

Access is Monday-Friday 2pm to 5pm.

Higher Mill. A tank bed beam engine was just about the most compact form of beam engine design. In common with most old engines the cylinder is unlagged. The central belt around the cylinder carries exhaust steam en-route to the condenser.

HOLLYCOMBE HOUSE, Liphook, Hants

An extensive private museum owned by Commander J. M. Baldock with a variety of stationary, portable, traction engines and railway locomotives as well as steam driven fairground 'rides'. Access is May-September on Sunday afternoons.

COMPOUND OVERTYPE SEMI-PORTABLE
ENGINE
Robey & Co, Lincoln 1914, No 33810, piston valve(HP), slide valve(LP), governor controlled expansion valve gear, air cooled condenser, Cornish multi-tubular boiler, superheater, feed-water heater.

The semi-portable engine was mainly a product of the manufacturers from eastern England and was virtually a 'packaged' power plant comprising a complete engine and boiler unit. In this the engine is mounted on top of the boiler hence 'overtype', but 'undertype' was also made with cylinders beneath the smokebox and the crankshaft immediately in front of the firebox. In the UK both types were popular in sawmills where the ample boiler proportions allowed steam to be maintained on waste wood. The semi-portable was much used in the former Colonies for all kinds of duties, eg winding at mines, sawmilling, electricity generation and so on. Requiring only a simple level base to stand on it was easy to instal and relatively easy to move to a new location when its work was done. Robeys built the semi-portable up to 200hp and the larger sizes could be very sophisticated as is this example with cut-off control, condenser, superheater and feed heading from the exhaust steam. Although many engines were built with the Cornish multi-tubular boiler a locomotive type boiler was also general practice. On small sizes engines were often single cylinder with the exhaust discharging to the chimney to assist the draught.

The engine at Hollycombe powered a sawmill throughout World War I and then in 1918 was installed at the works of Beechwood Brushes where for 50 years it drove the machinery and was fired on wood waste. In preservation the engine drives a rack saw bench, reverting once more to its original function. The air cooled condenser with fan driven by a Reader high-speed enclosed engine was useful in countries where water was scarce or of poor quality.

SINGLE CYLINDER HORIZONTAL ENGINE
T. Robinson, Rochdale, 9in × 18in. Vertical cross-tube boiler.

Although as yet unrestored, it is intended to use this engine to drive the collection of barn machinery. The engine and boiler spent their working lives at Basing House, Petersfield where it drove a well pump. Transmission was by gearing and a lengthy run of flat rods in a tunnel to the well head, where the motion was transformed to the vertical to drive the pump at the bottom of the well shaft.

J. HOLROYD & CO, Rochdale, Lancs

SINGLE BEAM MILL ENGINE
FROM WHITELEES MILL, LITTLEBOROUGH
Petrie & Co, Rochdale, 1841, 25in × 60in, divided slide valves, single plate cast-iron beam, gear drive to mill, 34 rpm, 40 psi.

Supplied to John Hurst of Whitelees Mill this engine worked with little alteration for 101 years. The only major replacement was the crankshaft, a wrought iron one replacing the original cast iron one. Each end of the cylinder has its own slide valve, although worked by a common valve spindle. The top and bottom valve chests are connected by twin perpendicular pipes of Doric style. Speed control was by slow speed Watt-type governor acting on a throttle valve. The engine is house built and designed for 20 nominal horse power at 20psi. With pressure raised to 40psi it actually developed 125hp.

The Holroyd gear works occupy the former Whitehall Street premises of Petrie & Co, and subsequent to the engine becoming redundant was re-erected in a specially built glass-fronted engine house. It may be seen at all times from the street.

LOUGHBOROUGH UNIVERSITY, Leics

SIX-COLUMN SINGLE BEAM WATERWORKS
PUMPING ENGINE
James Watt & Co, Birmingham, 1850.

This small, but attractive, engine was in service from 1850 to 1933 at a London waterworks. It was presented to the university in 1934 by the Metropolitan Water Board. Preserved alongside is a Cornish boiler without its brickwork setting. The engine is situated by the main entrance to the university.

MONKS HALL MUSEUM, Eccles, Lancs

A small museum begun by Eccles Borough Council and now administered by the City of Salford. The engineering section is likewise small and contains items of locally made machinery. The museum is open on weekdays.

INVERTED VERTICAL HIGH SPEED COMPOUND ENCLOSED ENGINE
Browett, Lindley & Co Ltd, Sandon Engine Works, Patricroft, 1930, No 3380, 150 hp, 500 rpm.

One of the crankcase doors has been replaced by a perspex panel allowing the working parts of the engine to be seen. This shows the cranks set at 180°, normal practice on high-speed engines, giving good reciprocating and rotating balance. A single piston valve of ingenious design controls admission and exhaust for *both* cylinders.

STEAM HAMMER
James Nasmyth, Patricroft, 1851.

Few steam hammers are available for public inspection and it is appropriate that one should be displayed close to the works where the first hammer was made. This example was in use until 1951.

◀ *Monk's Hall Museum. Nasmyth steam hammer which saw over one hundred years service.*

Loughborough University. With ▶ the pump chamber at ground level and the engine on a platform above, the whole of this James Watt pumping engine can be viewed easily.

NATIONAL MINING MUSEUM,

Lound Hall, Nr Bevercotes Colliery, Retford, Notts

TWIN CYLINDER HORIZONTAL COLLIERY WINDING ENGINE FROM DONISTHORPE COLLIERY, LEICESTERSHIRE
Maker and date unknown. Rebuilt Worsley Mesnes Ironworks, Wigan, 26 in × 54 in, piston valves, Gooch valve gear, 13 ft diameter parallel winding drum, Melling's controller, Worsley Mesnes reversing engine, 100 winds per hour, 256 yards, 80 psi.

The Leicestershire collieries were not particularly large or deep but they were very productive and the winding engines had plenty to do. From 1953 the engine wound a single 2½-ton mine car which by minimising decking time enabled the prodigious winding rate to be achieved. The engine was installed at Donisthorpe about 1905 but it may have been second hand. It had at least two partial rebuilds by Worsley Mesnes Ironworks which included the fitting of new piston valve cylinders. There are no refinements such as governor controlled cut-off and the cylinders took steam for about 85 per cent of the stroke. As part of a general colliery reorganisation which included the driving of a conveyor drift to the surface, the engine was replaced in 1977.

SINGLE CYLINDER HORIZONTAL ROTATIVE PUMPING ENGINE FROM ELLISTOWN COLLIERY, LEICESTERSHIRE
Maker and date obscure, Rebuilt Fraser & Chalmers, Erith, 13 in × 36 in, Corliss valves with trip gear. Flywheel 12 ft diameter, rope drive to countershaft, flat rods to angle bobs at shaft top.

Possibly originating as a mill engine this engine was installed at Ellistown Colliery as part of a joint pumping scheme between the colliery company and Coalville Urban District Council. The company had their pit drained and the council took the water and after treatment put it into public supply. The pumping plant remained in occasional use until about 1975

National Mining Museum. The driving side of the Donisthorpe Colliery winding engine when at work. At one hundred winds per hour the engineman's job was no sinecure, requiring constant alertness.

and its survival is reputed to be due to the legal complications of ownership. The colliery had wanted to be rid of it long before.

TWIN CYLINDER DIAGONAL CAPSTAN ENGINE FROM SHIREBROOK COLLIERY, NOTTS
Maker unknown, c 1896, 9 in × 12 in slide valves.

Capstan or winch engines were provided at most colliery shafts to assist in maintenance work, rope changing etc. The diagonal arrangement of the engine saved space although most capstans were in fact horizontal.

The National Mining Museum is run by the National Coal Board and is located at Lound Hall close to Bevercotes Colliery, about six miles south of Retford. Opening times are the first Sunday afternoon in the month throughout the year, but for a trial period the museum will be open Tuesdays to Saturdays as well. It is the intention to run the engines under steam from time to time, temporarily from a steam generator, but a permanent installation of a Cornish boiler is to be made.

National Mining Museum. The Donisthorpe Colliery winding engine when in service. The long stroke usual in colliery winding engines is evident by the length of the cylinder.

NATIONAL RAILWAY MUSEUM, York

Although famous for its collection of railway locomotives and rolling stock, the museum also possesses two distinctive and venerable stationary engines. Both engines were in railway service as winding engines on inclines too steep for satisfactory locomotive operation, especially in the early days.

SINGLE CYLINDER HORIZONTAL WINDING ENGINE
FROM SWANNINGTON INCLINE, LEICESTERSHIRE
Horsley Iron & Coal Co, 1833, 18¼ in × 42 in, piston valve, gab valve gear, lattice eccentric rod, 80 psi.

The Swannington engine was designed by Robert Stephenson for the Leicester & Swannington Railway and was in service from 1833 to 1946. It is the oldest known surviving engine with a piston valve. The gab valve gear has a foot pedal for disengaging the eccentric rod, and 'barrow handles' for working the valve to obtain reverse rotation. A band brake operating on a drum fixed to the crankshaft controlled the descending load on the 1 in 17 single-track incline. For many years steam was supplied by a second-hand boiler from a Midland Railway Johnson 0-6-0 goods locomotive.

SINGLE CYLINDER VERTICAL WINDING ENGINE
FROM WEATHERHILL INCLINE, Co DURHAM
1833, 29 in × 60 in

Built for the Stanhope & Tyne Railway (later part of the North Eastern Railway) this engine is a variation of the traditional Durham winder applied to haulage on a railway incline.

National Railway Museum. The Swannington Incline winding engine as it was in 1923. The cylindrical steam chest for the piston valve is seen above the cylinder. Crown Copyright

NEWCASTLE-UPON-TYNE MUSEUM OF SCIENCE & ENGINEERING, Exhibition Park

The museum has a number of mainly small engines on display including a steam turbine of early vintage. For some years the museum has had a large collection of engines in store including some early turbines and marine reciprocating engines. The collection is being moved to larger premises, a former CWS warehouse in West Blandford Street, where engines will be available for public viewing. For the time being some engines will remain at Exhibition Park.

The stationary engines (marine engines are not included in this list) at present on display at Exhibition Park are as follows:

SIX-COLUMN CONDENSING BEAM ENGINE FROM TENNANT'S BREWERY, GLASGOW
Maker unknown, c1820, 13 in × 26 in (approx), slide valve.

GRASSHOPPER ENGINE (FROM PLESSEY MILL)
Maker unknown, c1830, slide valve.

TANK BED A-FRAME BEAM ENGINE FROM GLEMSFORD SILK MILL
J. T. Beale, Greenwich, 1849, slide valve.

SINGLE CYLINDER INVERTED VERTICAL HIGH SPEED ENCLOSED ENGINE
Robey & Co, Lincoln, No 37197, 1914, 3½ in × 3 in, piston valve, 2½ hp at 700 rpm, direct coupled to Laurence Scott dynamo No 21334, 1 kW, 100 volts, 10 amps.

COMPOUND INVERTED VERTICAL HIGH SPEED ENCLOSED ENGINE (FROM YORK CITY ASYLUM)
Belliss & Morcom, Birmingham, No 2657, 1905, 7½ in (HP), 12 in (LP) × 6 in stroke, piston valve, direct coupled to Westinghouse dynamo 33 kW, 230 volts, 140 amps.

SINGLE CYLINDER INVERTED VERTICAL ENGINE FROM GATESHEAD TECHNICAL COLLEGE HEAT ENGINES LABORATORY
Robey & Co, Lincoln, No 52134, 1951, 6½ in × 9 in, Meyer expansion slide valve, surface condenser and electrically driven air pump.

STEAM TURBINE (FROM FORTH BANK POWER STATION)
C. A. Parsons, Newcastle, 1900, parallel flow turbine, electric governor, 500 kW at 2,700 rpm.

The stationary engines intended to be on display at West Blandford Street are shown in the list below. Again only 'land based' engines are included, but marine engines will also be displayed.

SINGLE CYLINDER A-FRAME VERTICAL ENGINE
T. Richardson, 1876, 3 in × 5 in, slide valve, Stephenson's link motion.

Made by a knowledgable blacksmith this engine appears to have been used to drive a small workshop. A hand-cut pinion wheel is fitted on the crankshaft to transmit the drive. The link motion, which is probably a late addition, is very lightly made and gives inaccurate valve events.

TWIN CYLINDER SINGLE COLUMN BEAM BLOWING ENGINE FROM ALBERT HALL, LONDON
Penn & Co, Greenwich, 1876, 7 in × 24 in, slide valves, blowing tubs 24 in × 24 in, 1½ psi.

Blowing engines are usually associated with ironworks and blast furnaces, but this small engine blew the organ at the Albert Hall.

SINGLE CYLINDER SCOTCH CRANK ENGINE
Maker unknown, c1875, 4 in × 4½, slide valve.

This little engine was sold at the dispersal sale of the Thames Ironworks in 1913. As the crankpin operates in a slot in the crosshead and there is no connecting rod, the piston moves with harmonic motion. The arrangement was used mainly in small pumps and as there is no connecting rod the length of the engine is kept to a minimum.

STEAM TURBINES
Clarke Chapman, Parsons & Co, No 195, 1888, double flow centre inlet type, magnetic governor, 24 kW, 5,000 rpm.

C. A. Parsons, Newcastle, 1891, 4,000 rpm, originally drove 100 kW dynamo.

C. A. Parsons, Newcastle, No 618, 12 kW turbo-generator.

Greenwood & Batley, Leeds, c1945, Single-stage 'Laval' impulse turbine, originally drove a gas booster.

Societe Rateau, Paris, c1950, single-stage 'Rateau' turbine, originally drove a gas booster.

TWIN CYLINDER VERTICAL HYDRAULIC PUMPING ENGINE
FROM TYNE SWING BRIDGE
Armstrong, Mitchell & Co, Newcastle, No 303, 1876, 7 in × 10 in, slide valves.

INVERTED VERTICAL SINGLE CYLINDER HIGH SPEED ENCLOSED ENGINE (Sectioned)
FROM ORMSKIRK POOR LAW INSTITUTE & BROOMFLEET BRICKWORKS
Browett, Lindley & Co, Patricroft, No 2885, c1910, $9\frac{1}{2}$ × $7\frac{1}{2}$ in, piston valve, direct coupled to Electric Construction Co dynamo 40 kW, 220 volts, 180 amps.

INVERTED VERTICAL BANJO PUMP
Robey & Co, Lincoln, No 3091, c1880, No 2 size, 3 in × 3 in steam cylinder.

INVERTED VERTICAL SIMPLEX DIRECT ACTING PUMP
G. & J. Weir Ltd, Cathcart, 1960, $4\frac{1}{2}$ × 3 in.

SINGLE CYLINDER CAMERON PUMP
J. Cameron, Manchester, c1885, 4 in × 3 in × 2 in, slide valve, 130 rpm, 520 gall/hr.

INVERTED VERTICAL TRIPLE EXPANSION ENGINE
FROM SUNDERLAND TECHNICAL COLLEGE HEAT ENGINES LABORATORY
A. G. Mumford & Co, Colchester.

CYLINDER OF TWIN HORIZONTAL WINDING ENGINE (Sectioned)
FROM WOODHORN COLLIERY
Grant, Ritchie & Co, Kilmarnock, 1900, left-hand cylinder 28 in × 72 in with drop valves.

SINGLE CYLINDER HORIZONTAL ENGINE
FROM BRIMROD STEAM LAUNDRY
Probably Petrie & Co, Rochdale, c1899, 13 in × 24 in, slide valve, Pickering governor.

SINGLE CYLINDER HORIZONTAL ENGINE (Sectioned)
E. Green & Co, Wakefield, 5 in × 10 in, slide valve, 5 hp, 126 rpm, 100 psi.

HORIZONTAL DUPLEX DIRECT ACTING PUMPS (2)
Worthington-Simpson Ltd, Newark-on-Trent, $4\frac{1}{2}$ in × $2\frac{1}{4}$ in × 4 in.
Lee, Howl & Co, Tipton, c1930, 6 in × 6 in × 6 in.

SINGLE CYLINDER HORIZONTAL 'BANJO' TAR PUMP
FROM DUNSTON GASWORKS
Joseph Evans, Wolverhampton, No 11164.

TWIN CYLINDER A-FRAME DIAGONAL ENGINE
J. Wood, Ramsbottom, c1900.

NORTH OF ENGLAND OPEN AIR MUSEUM, Beamish, Co Durham
The Museum has been established to provide an authentic representation of life in the North East of England in the nineteenth and early twentieth centuries. As part of the general scene a representative colliery has been reconstructed including the engine and its house from the former Beamish pit.

SINGLE CYLINDER VERTICAL COLLIERY WINDING ENGINE
FROM BEAMISH COLLIERY
J. & G. Joicey, 1855, 24 in × 60 in, Cornish valves, plug-rod valve gear, parallel motion to crosshead, wood lagged winding drum.

Phineas Crowther patented his vertical engine in 1800. It was a major breakaway from the beam engine design and achieved great popularity as a colliery winding engine. Although it was used all over Britain, nowhere was it

Beamish. Cylinder and massive timber A-frame of the Durham-type winder.

more popular than in the North East, its birthplace. Capable of giving a faster wind than a beam engine, it enabled output to be greatly increased without the need to sink more shafts. The ultimate development was the twin-cylinder vertical winding engine.

The Crowther or Durham-type winding engine was generally used with flat winding ropes and a counterweight in a staple, or subsidiary shaft, at the back of the engine house. This counterweight was to assist starting and landing. The Beamish engine however has a drum for round-section ropes and there is no counterweight. Typical of the Durham winding engines is the tall engine house, once a familiar sight in the coalfield. The engine is house built with a timber A-frame to give additional support to the crankshaft. At the start of each wind the valve gear was worked by hand and years of operation has worn finger-shaped grooves in the handles.

Beamish. Plug rod valve gear of Durham type winding engine. Restoration was in progress and the gear is incomplete. Note the finger grooves worn in the handles – a result of years of operation.

TWIN CYLINDER HORIZONTAL MINE SHAFT
SINKING WINCH
Close, Burlinson & Co, Sunderland, 1868,
slide valves, Stephenson's valve gear.

A sinking winch comprises two engines which are virtually small winding engines. One engine (the upper) is used for winding the kibble or hoppit which, shaped like a large bucket, is used for removing the spoil as sinking progresses. The kibble is also used for lowering materials and tools down the shaft and for carrying men at the beginning and end of shifts.

The second and lower engine has its winding ropes attached by chains to a working platform suspended some little way above the shaft bottom. The platform is used by men installing the shaft lining, which was once of brickwork but now nearly always of concrete. The 'sinkers' work in the shaft bottom underneath the platform. The kibble engine is in use constantly, but the platform engine is used only when the working platform requires to be moved. The engines forming this sinking winch were used to sink the shaft at Silksworth Colliery in 1868.

The Beamish Museum is open daily during June, July and August and, except Monday, at other times. Hours vary according to time of year.

NORTHERN MILL ENGINES SOCIETY
MUSEUM, Mornington Road, Bolton, Lancs
The Society has leased two former engine houses at Atlas Mill for the re-erection of engines taken from various mills in Lancashire and Yorkshire. Messrs Robert Mason are the owners of the mill, which now makes fireplaces and other building products. Mr Mason is President of the Society which has so far erected three engines, all of which can be run under steam provided by the Messrs Mason works boiler. Access is on Open Days, and most Sundays.

INVERTED VERTICAL COMPOUND NON-
DEAD-CENTRE ENGINE
FROM PARK ST SHED, RADCLIFFE, LANCS
John Musgrave & Sons, Bolton, 1893, 10 in
(HP), 18 in (LP), × 18 in stroke, semi-rotary
slide valves, Pickering governor, flywheel 8 ft
diameter, rope pulley 6 ft diameter grooved for
six ropes, 150 rpm.

The non-dead-centre engine (Fleming & Ferguson's patent) was a Musgrave speciality. It was built in a variety of sizes, many of the large ones being in twin engine form arranged as quadruple expansion. This compound engine was the smallest one built and is also the sole survivor. The governor operates a throttle valve, but the larger engines had Corliss valves and cut-off control. Without going into the geometric details the principle of the triangular connecting rod was to enable the engine to start in virtually any position of the crank. Fleming & Ferguson made *their* engines for marine duty where the starting feature was very advantageous.

At Park Street shed the exhaust was to a condenser, with the air pump driven by a rocking arm from the connecting rod. This rocking arm is part of the geometry of the connecting rod and serves as a constraint or guide at the point of attachment. The engine was the first to be re-erected by the Society and is now run regularly under steam although exhaust is now direct to atmosphere.

Northern Mill Engines Museum. The now unique Musgrave non-dead-centre engine. A very compact layout useful in marine service for which the design originated.

CROSS-COMPOUND BEAM ENGINE
FROM CROSSFIELD MILL, WARDLE, LANCS
Maker unknown, possibly John Petrie, Rochdale, c1840, rebuilt 1893, slide valves, Watt-type governor, single plate cast-iron beams, gear drive.

Cross-compound beam engines were not uncommon in the textile industry but appear to have been quite rare elsewhere. This engine may well be the only survivor of its type. In its working location the engine had cast-iron columns as additional support for the entablature. The columns remain but not the engine house walls. The flywheel is in the form of a spur wheel, and part of the mill shaft with its pinion meshing into the flywheel has been retained. Governor speed control is by throttle valve. The engine can be run under steam.

Northern Mill Engines Museum. Cross compound beam engine. House-built, but now standing independently for display. Note the gear drive to the mill main shaft – closely allied to watermill practice.

Northern Mill Engines Museum. J. & W. McNaught tandem compound engine in course of re-erection.

HORIZONTAL TANDEM COMPOUND MILL ENGINE
FROM WASP MILL, WARDLE, LANCS
J. & W. McNaught, Rochdale, 1902, 13 in (HP), 26 in (LP) × 36 in stroke, Corliss valves HP, slide valve LP, flywheel 14 ft diameter grooved for eight ropes, 250 hp, 76 rpm. Named *Elsie*.

Elsie is typical of very many engines built by various makers for the weaving sheds of East Lancashire, and she went to Wasp Mill second hand in 1917. The high-pressure cylinder is behind the low pressure and the LP exhausts into a jet condenser below the engine bed. The air pump is driven by a link and rocking lever from the crosshead. Speed control is by cross-arm governor. Restoration has been of a very high standard and the engine can be run under steam.

NORTH WESTERN MUSEUM OF SCIENCE & INDUSTRY, Grosvenor Street, Manchester
At present operating in restricted premises, this museum has three small engines on display, two of which are run regularly under steam. Several important large engines from the surrounding area are held in store and hopefully it will be possible to display these in larger premises from 1985 onwards.

GRASSHOPPER ENGINE
Maker unknown, c1830, 6½ in × 30 in, flywheel 9 ft diameter, beam 4 ft 4 in between centres.

The grasshopper engine achieved considerable popularity where relatively small power was needed. The beam support was pivotted at the bottom to allow lateral movement of the beam fulcrum, while the other end of the beam to which the piston was attached was guided in a straight line by parallel motion. With the connecting rod taken from a point about midway between fulcrum and piston rod the engine was rather more compact than a conventional beam engine. Many of these engines were made in small workshops with limited equipment and the poor quality of this particular engine highlights this. Nevertheless they worked and this one can still be run under steam.

SINGLE CYLINDER VERTICAL A-FRAME ENGINE
Maker unknown c1840, approx 5 hp.

A fully restored and workable example of the once popular small vertical engine.

TWIN CYLINDER DIAGONAL ENGINE
John Wood, Ramsbottom, c1900

Diagonal engines of this type were used extensively for driving textile finishing machinery before the advent of small electric motors.

GLADSTONE POTTERY MUSEUM,
Longton, Staffs

TANDEM COMPOUND MILL ENGINE
Marshall & Sons, Gainsborough, No 32967,
1900, drop valve inlet, Corliss valve exhaust,
Hartnell high-speed governor, girder bed, disc
crank, belt drive.

Marshall's made a point in their sales literature
about their own patent trip gear and double-
beat drop valves, usually showing valves
driven from a geared side-shaft. They did
however make Corliss valve engines and this
engine is a combination of the two. It was a
useful arrangement as all moving parts could
be kept above floor level. The trip gear is
Proell's.

The inlet valves are driven from an eccentric
on the crankshaft, the eccentric rod operating a
short rocking shaft between the inlet valves.
Lifting arms on the rocking shafts open the
valves, which are then released by trip gear.
The governor controls the trip gear on the HP
cylinder, the LP trip gear being hand adjusted.
The Corliss exhaust valves are directly driven
from a second eccentric on the crankshaft. As a

further aid to economy the cylinders are steam
jacketed, any condensate forming in the jackets
being drained away by 'steam traps' which
release water while holding back steam. The
disc crank and girder bed are typical Marshall
features and were also popular with other
Lincolnshire manufacturers. The girder bed
made for a very strong and rigid engine. The
engine was brought here from Harrison &
Mayer, Potters' millers of Phoenix Works,
Hanley, when the Gladstone works became a
museum and was re-erected alongside the slip
house.

Gladstone works was in use until the 1960s
and after it had closed down, a Trust was
formed to preserve it as representative of a
traditional Victorian Pottery. The slip
machinery, and with it the engine, is turned by
a concealed motor for demonstration purposes.
Access is daily April-September and except
Mondays at other times.

*Gladstone Pottery. Marshall's favoured drop
valves which were fitted to a wide range of engine
sizes, and around the turn of the century they
used Corliss valves on exhaust, while fitting drop
valves on the inlet.*

NOTTINGHAM INDUSTRIAL MUSEUM, Wollaton Park

> WOOLF COMPOUND WATERWORKS PUMPING ENGINE
> R. & W. Hawthorn, Newcastle-upon-Tyne, 1858, 18½ in × 4 ft 6 in (HP), 31¾ in × 6 ft (LP), Cornish valves, twin-plate cast-iron beam 23 ft long, flywheel 18 ft diameter. Two force pumps, one well pump, bucket diameter 15 in, stroke 5 ft, 0·5 mgd, 12 rpm, 40 psi.

One of two Hawthorn Woolf compound engines installed at Basford works in the northern suburbs of Nottingham. The engine was in service until the 1960s. Pumping was from a well sunk 110 ft into the heavily water bearing Bunter Sandstone. Delivery was to two service reservoirs, one force pump supplying each reservoir. The larger force pump (17½ in diameter × 3 ft stroke) has a cast-iron cruciform section pump rod.

At Wollaton Park the engine has been re-erected in a large glass building with the advantage that one can go inside the house as well as look in from the outside. Access is daily and the engine is run under steam on the last Sunday of each month and on Bank Holidays.

POOLE, Dorset. The Arndale Centre

> HORIZONTAL CROSS-COMPOUND MILL ENGINE
> FROM SYDENHAM SAWMILL, HAMWORTHY
> Wren & Hopkinson, c1880, 10 in (HP), 18 in (LP) × 24 in stroke, flywheel 8 ft diameter, jet condenser.

An interesting engine because it is a cross-compound in the lower power range. Victorian engineers considered economy in operation a virtue even at the bottom end of the power scale. This engine was removed from the sawmill in 1970 by the Poole Industrial Archeology Society, to be re-erected to form the centre-piece of the new Arndale shopping precinct.

Royal Scottish Museum. Cylinder and valve gear of the 1786 Boulton & Watt rotative beam engine. The plug rod and handle valve gear was used on all early beam engines, but eccentric-driven valve gear later became normal on rotative engines.

ROYAL SCOTTISH MUSEUM, Edinburgh

The Royal Scottish Museum was established in the 1860s and the engineering section was intended to show contemporary practice. The many models of engines were made in the museum workshops contemporary with the full-size examples, from drawings supplied or lent by the manufacturers. As time went by however aspects of past engineering were

included and as old full-size engines have become available they have been included in the collection. Some of the engines spent their working lives in local industry.

SINGLE CYLINDER BEAM ENGINE
FROM BARCLAY & PERKINS BREWERY, SOUTHWARK
Boulton & Watt, Soho Works, Birmingham, 1786, 25 in × 48 in, single beat drop valves, plug rod valve gear, sun & planet crank, wooden beam, flywheel 16 ft diameter.

A classic early Boulton & Watt double-acting rotative engine. The valves are lifted by toggles which receive their motion from arbors operated by the plug rod. The alignment of the toggles is carefully arranged to give the maximum lifting effort at the instant of opening the valves. Although the engineers and craftsmen of the day had limited equipment in the way of machine tools they built well and this engine was in use for 99 years.

SIX-COLUMN TANK-BED SINGLE BEAM ENGINE
FROM COBB & CO, MARGATE BREWERY
Maker unknown, c1826, 'long D' slide valve, Watt-type governor, single plate cast-iron beam, cruciform connecting rod, four-spoke flywheel.

Tank-bed engines were often built by small works with limited equipment. Finish could be somewhat crude, as in this example with its square-ended crank. The long-D slide valve gave short ports between steam chest and cylinder — an aid to efficiency — but its large area made it suitable only for low-pressure steam, otherwise excessive friction resulted. Traditionally this engine is said to have been salvaged from a shipwreck off the Kent coast, the engine being destined for foreign shores. Its dousing did not affect its future performance for it was used until 1950.

Royal Scottish Museum. Tank bed six-column beam engine with eccentric driven valve gear, long 'D' slide valve and a four-arm flywheel.

SINGLE COLUMN BEAM ENGINE FROM G. MACKAY & Co, ST LEONARD'S BREWERY, EDINBURGH

Maker and date unknown, 7½ in × 14 in, slide valve, Watt-type governor, single plate cast-iron beam, 4 ft centres; flywheel 3 ft 9 in diameter.

Beam engines were made down to very small ones. This little engine was probably one of a number produced by its makers, for the bedplate is suitable for engines of 'either hand', registers being formed for bearing pedestals on both sides of the bed. The engine was second-hand to the brewery in 1867 and worked until 1933. The flywheel appears to be of relatively recent origin. Finish generally is neat and workmanlike, but quite plain.

GRASSHOPPER BEAM ENGINE FROM BRIGHTON COUNTY BOROUGH MENTAL HOSPITAL, HAYWARDS HEATH, SUSSEX

Built 1860, 6 in × 12 in, slide valve, cast-iron beam, 4 ft centres, flywheel 6 ft diameter, 6 hp, 25 psi.

An interesting contrast to the single-column beam engine of similar size exhibited adjacent. The grasshopper design is rather more compact and was popular in its day for small powers. The cylinder casting has Grecian fluting but there is little other ornamentation, and the flywheel has a rounded rim typical of many old engines. At the hospital the engine drove well pumps for 68 years.

SINGLE CYLINDER HORIZONTAL ENGINE FROM ST ANN'S BREWERY, EDINBURGH

Maker unknown, c1875, 8 in × 18 in, wood-lagged cylinder, slide valve, disc crank, Watt-type governor, flywheel 4 ft diameter.

The date of this engine should be treated with some reserve and it may well be older. Although the maker is unknown almost without doubt the engine was made in Edinburgh. Features to note are the forked little-end of the connecting rod and the very small steam chest. The flywheel appears small and relatively modern and out of keeping with the rest of the engine. It may be that the engine was second hand to the brewery and that a smaller flywheel was fitted so that the engine would go into available space. It was certainly a tight fit! The engine survived a fire and closure of the

Royal Scottish Museum. Single-column beam engine with slide valve at the rear of the cylinder driven by eccentric and rocker arms from the crankshaft.

Royal Scottish Museum. Grasshopper beam engine with the beam pivotted at the top of a vertical swinging column seen on left of picture.

brewery. In 1979 it was presented to the museum by Scottish & Newcastle Breweries and, following a highly creditable job of restoration by the brewery company, was placed on display. The engine's job at the brewery was to drive well pumps and these were operated from the engine crankshaft by a system of gearing and rods.

The steeple engine obtains its name from the resemblance of the frame to a church spire. It was one of the early attempts to break away from the beam engine design to give a more compact power unit while retaining a vertical cylinder. In Britain it was generally made in small sizes only and the subsequent success of the horizontal engine made the design obsolete; nevertheless the action was quite fascinating and many engines gave long service. This engine worked until 1931. The Pickering governor will be a modification made during the engine's working life.

Royal Scottish Museum. Steeple engine with the cast iron frame showing how this type of engine got its name.

THE SCIENCE MUSEUM,
South Kensington, London

One of the leading museums of science and industry in the world, the Science Museum started from humble beginnings during the nineteenth century in Brompton, where a collection of early locomotives, engines and other machinery was gathered together. In common with most museums of this type the exhibits are static but certain of them can be turned by an electric motor. The following gives details of the principal exhibits, but does not pretend to be complete. With such a large collection some reorganisation is always taking place. The full-size collection is supplemented by an excellent range of models.

Access is daily including Sundays.

An example of the Newcomen-type engine, which post-dates some of the Boulton & Watt 'separate condenser' engines in the collection. This serves to show that the new and more efficient type of engine did not sweep the board to the total exclusion of the older type. The atmospheric engine continued to be built for service in collieries where there was an abundant supply of unsaleable fuel. It must be remembered that at this time it was illegal to sell 'slack' and what was not used was actually burnt to waste. In these circumstances it is not surprising that the atmospheric engine persisted, for it was simpler and cheaper to build, easier to look after and there were no patent royalties to pay.

This engine was built for Oakerthorpe Colliery in Derbyshire and as erected had the then usual wooden beam. Its builder was one of the leading steam engineers of the day. When moved to Pentrich Colliery the wooden beam was replaced by cast-iron and three pump rods were attached to the outdoor arch-head by chains. Each pump rod operated a separate lift of pumps. Shear legs over the shaft enabled rods and pumps to be lifted out and replaced; the shear legs have been re-erected at the museum. When working steam was provided by haystack boilers and a single haystack boiler is exhibited with the engine to illustrate the general layout.

This very early James Watt engine has many
details which were later developed in the
Cornish pumping engine, while retaining con-
structional features of the Newcomen engine,
eg wooden arch-head beam and chains connecting the piston and pump rods to the beam.
Steam pressure (greatly assisted by vacuum)
now lifted the pump rods, while the engine was
worked on the outdoor stroke by the weight of
the pump rods with the piston in equilibrium.
An equilibrium valve put both sides of the
piston in communication at the end of the
steam stroke. The first application of the steam
engine to rotative motion for driving machinery was to pump water from the tailrace to the
headrace of a waterwheel. Newcomen and
James Watt engines were used for this purpose
and this is the duty which *Old Bess* performed
until taken out of use in 1848.

Adam Heslop patented a design of engine in
which a closed cylinder of the Watt type took
steam from the boiler. After completion of the
piston stroke the steam was exhausted to a
Newcomen-type atmospheric cylinder. This
system was held to infringe the Watt separate
condenser patent but nevertheless Heslop
built a number of engines for use in the North
of England coalfields and several were erected
in the Shropshire coalfield also. This engine
was presented to the museum in 1878 and was
stated to be the last Heslop engine to remain at
work, but this statement led to the discovery of
others, and the Madeley Wood collieries in
Shropshire continued to use Heslop engines
until 1890.

JAMES WATT ROTATIVE BEAM ENGINE
FROM MATTHEW BOULTON, SOHO WORKS
Boulton & Watt, 1788, 18¾ in × 48 in, wooden
beam, parallel motion, cast-iron connecting
rod, plug rod valve-gear, sun and planet crank,
toothed rim flywheel 15 ft diameter, 13¾ ihp,
the *Lap Engine*.

This engine embodies the major inventions of
James Watt's double acting cylinder, separate
condenser, parallel motion, sun and planet
gear and the application of the steam engine to
give true rotative motion. The sun and planet
crank arrangement however was one of necessity as someone else (William Pickard) held the
patent for the true crank. Watt abandoned the
sun and planet gear once the patent for the
crank had expired. The engine drove lapping
or polishing machinery for silverware at the
Soho Works, hence the name. The valve
nozzles were renewed in 1833 and the engine
remained in service until 1858.

JAMES WATT ROTATIVE BEAM ENGINE
FROM ATKINSON'S CHEMICAL WORKS,
ALDERSGATE ST, LONDON
Boulton & Watt, 1797, 19¼ in × 48 in, plug rod
valve-gear, cam cut-off gear, wooden beam,
wooden connecting rod, sun and planet crank,
parallel motion, flywheel 12 ft diameter, 7 psi.

Another survivor of James Watt's early engines. The cylinder is a replacement of 1806,
the original cylinder being 16 in × 48 in. A cam
cut-off gear is fitted allowing expansive use of
steam. It is unlikely that this is original, as
although Watt was aware of the expansive
properties of steam he found no advantage in
its use due to the very low steam pressures then
employed. The date of fitting the cut-off gear is
unknown, but possibly it was at the time of
renewal of the cylinder. The wooden connecting rod with its many strengthening straps is
worthy of note. There appears to have been
some difficulty with the condenser and additional auxiliary pumps have been provided.

BOULTON & WATT ROTATIVE BEAM ENGINE
Boulton & Watt, c1807, plug rod valve-gear,
cast-iron beam, crank.

An engine which illustrates the progress made
in 20 years or so of engine design. Although the
valve gear is still plug-rod operated the beam is
now cast-iron and an ordinary crank is used.

SEMI-PORTABLE ENGINE
Hazeldine & Co, Bridgnorth, No 14, c1803-8,
6·37 in ×30½ in, plug rod valve-gear, flywheel
9 ft diameter, 50 rpm approx, 52 psi, return-
flue boiler.

Possibly this is one of the most important
survivors of the early engines. It embodies all
the principles of Richard Trevithick — high
pressure steam, non-condensing — which enabled the development of locomotives, portable and traction engines to proceed. This
engine itself is reasonably portable, the boiler
forming the bed for the engine, which has its
single vertical cylinder let into the top of the
horizontal boiler shell. We owe the existence of
this engine to Mr F. W. Webb, Chief Mechanical Engineer of the London & North Western Railway who discovered it in 1882 amongst
some scrap at Hereford. Realising its worth he
had it transported to Crewe Works where a
number of missing parts were replaced. Subsequently the engine was presented to the
museum. A feature to note on the engine is the
method of securing the boiler front plate to the
boiler barrel by large square-headed bolts and
nuts.

WOOLF COMPOUND A-FRAME BEAM ENGINE
J. & E. Hall, Dartford, c1838, 7½ in ×20½ in
(HP), 15 in × 30 in (LP), slide valves, single
plate cast-iron beam, tank bed, Watt-type
governor, originally 30 rpm, latterly 47 rpm,
80 psi, 25 hp.

A typical beam engine of the period built for
low powers. It is self contained with the
condenser and other auxiliaries contained in
the cast-iron tank bed. Note should be made of
the valve gear. The slide valves obtain their
motion from a Scotch crank mounted on a
layshaft underneath the cylinders, the layshaft
being driven by a shaft and bevel gearing from
the crankshaft.

INVERTED VERTICAL SINGLE CYLINDER
ENGINE
FROM KEW GARDENS
Marshall, Sons & Co Ltd, Gainsborough,
1891, 6½ in × 10 in, slide valve, crankshaft
governor, 210 rpm, 14 hp, 100 psi.

A refined type of small engine with the crankshaft governor giving cut-off control. This
gave the maximum economy possible with this
type of engine.

SINGLE CYLINDER VERTICAL OSCILLATING ENGINE
FROM METROPOLITAN WATER BOARD, HAMMERSMITH
Harvey & Co, Hayle, 1870, 5½ in × 10 in, slide valve.

The oscillating cylinder engine was once common in marine engineering, where large sizes were used in paddle steamers. On land its use was mainly confined to small sizes, often for driving individual machines. For these low power applications it was cheap, simple and compact. This Harvey engine was used to drive workshop machinery at Hammersmith and despite its small size it is typical of the maker's solid engineering.

CROSS COMPOUND HORIZONTAL MILL ENGINE
FROM PINSLEY VIEW MILL, HARLE SYKE, BURNLEY, LANCS
Burnley Ironworks, 1903, 17 in (HP), 35 in (LP) × 54 in stroke, Corliss valves, flywheel 18 ft diameter for eighteen ropes, jet condenser behind LP cylinder, 700 hp, 72 rpm, 160 psi, twin-cylinder vertical barring engine.

Pinsley View was a weaving shed with 1,400 looms. The typical Lancashire shed was considerably smaller than this, but in East Lancashire there were a number of mills having up to 2,000 looms. These mills needed engines to match, but even so most engines in the cotton trade were well overloaded at some time in their career. This particular engine would develp nearly 900 ihp quite easily. Although rather large for a 'shed' engine it is nevertheless typical of Lancashire practice and is the only large mill engine at present on display in a museum. It is also the last Burnley Ironworks engine as such, although a 'McNaughted' beam engine by predecessors William Bracewell is being re-erected in the museum at Bradford.

The Corliss valves are at the four corners of the cylinder castings, but Burnley Ironworks also built engines with all valves underneath the cylinders. They also rebuilt old slide valve engines and fitted all the Corliss valves on top. This did not allow good drainage and great care was needed when starting, but the centre lines of the old slide-valve engines did not allow for placing Corliss valves beneath the cylinders without extensive rebuilding.

TABLE ENGINE
FROM SPRINGFIELD HOSPITAL, TOOTING
Maudslay, Son & Field, London, 1840, 12 in × 24 in, slide valve, 60 rpm.

The table engine is a fascinating machine, and its design gives ample scope for decorative embellishment. As one would expect from this maker (Maudslay was the originator of the design), the finish is to a very high standard.

The table engine was widely used in the first half of the nineteenth century for low power applications. It was self contained and reasonably compact, with a vertical cylinder. At the hospital, this engine was used to drive a three-barrel pump in a 150 ft-deep well. Drive was from a countershaft gear driven from the engine crankshaft, thence by a system of flat rods, angle bobs and spears to the well pump.

INVERTED VERTICAL SINGLE ACTING HIGH SPEED ENCLOSED ENGINES:
Single Crank Triple Expansion Engine (Sectioned)
Two-crank compound engine from Chamber & Fargus, Kingston-upon-Hull
Willans & Robinson, c1888, 450 rpm, 18 hp, Siemens DC generator, 80 volts.

Developed and perfected during the 1870s by Willans, the single.acting high-speed engine was the first breakthrough into high revolutions in a steam engine. Splash lubrication from the crankcase oil bath prevented overheating and excessive wear of bearings, while with single-acting cylinders there was no reversal of stress and this prevented knocking. Steam distribution was by a unique central piston valve enclosed in a trunk which acted as the steam chest and also formed the piston rod. The eccentric for operating the valve was forged solid with the crankpin. Engines were available as simple, compound and triple expansion types, the compounding cylinders being mounted or stacked in tandem. Higher powers were obtained by making two- or three-crank engines.

The sectioned demonstration engine illustrates the unique features of the Willans central valve engine. An important feature to note is the trunk type crosshead and guide. The crosshead acted as an air compressor on the non-power stroke and ensured that there was a constant downward thrust on the crankpin.

The first engine with forced lubrication and an
important landmark in steam engine development. This was Charles Pain's patent of 1890
in which an oil pump forced oil through
passages in the crankshaft and crankpin, thus
preventing knocking and heating in spite of the
reversal of stress at each piston stroke. This
type of engine ousted the Willans type for
generation duties and achieved a great popularity. Other makers, eg Browett-Lindley,
Ashworth & Parker built very similar engines.
Engines in use today are mainly of this pattern
and new ones are still made from time to time.

A foretaste of what was to come, this turbo-
alternator set was supplied to a public electric
light supply company. The turbine bearings
are sealed by labyrinth glands (an early date for
their application), and again a forerunner of
general practice on turbines. A solenoid governor is fitted for speed control. The alternator
is a two-pole machine, while the speed of
4,800 rpm gives an alternating current frequency of 80 cycles per second (Hertz), compared with the now standard frequency of
50 Hz in the UK. The turbine is sectioned to
show the internal details.

A very small set by modern standards, the
turbine is remarkably compact with a surface
condenser in the bedplate. Forced lubrication
is provided for all bearings.

SOMERSET COUNTY MUSEUM,
Taunton Castle

Although not an engineering museum several
engines are displayed. These are mainly small,
with single-cylinder horizontal types predom-
inating; all are static exhibits. The main engine
exhibit described below can be turned by an
electric motor-

A relatively small engine, the entablature is
is formed of two cast-iron joists, supported
under the beam trunnion bearings by four
cast-iron columns. In its working location the
entablature was built into the engine house
walls, but as exhibited the entablature of
necessity is without this additional support.

STAFFORDSHIRE COUNTY MUSEUM,
Shugborough Hall, Great Haywood, Stafford

John Knowles operate fireclay mines and this
small engine was in use until the 1960s. It is
typical of engines formerly found at fireclay
mines in many places, eg Shropshire. Though
these steam plants may have been inefficient
they lasted a long time and made sense eco-
nomically. Often associated with the fireclay
bed would be a thin seam of coal, which was
very often of too poor a quality to be sold, but it
could be used to fire a boiler at the mine.

TOLSON MEMORIAL MUSEUM
Ravensknowle Park, Huddersfield, Yorks

A horizontal engine with the crankshaft behind
the cylinder. The connecting rod passes back
from the crosshead alongside the cylinder. The
idea behind the design was to save space. This
engine worked at a local brickworks.

Access is daily.

THE THURSFORD COLLECTION,
Thursford, Fakenham, Norfolk
This privately owned museum, the result of half a lifetime's effort by Mr George Cushing, concentrates on road locomotives and traction engines together with the mechanical organs used by travelling showmen and others. There are a few small stationary engines, but in any case with exhibits restored to such a superb standard the museum is worth repeated visits.

TWIN CYLINDER CENTRE ENGINE
Frederick Savage, King's Lynn, 1889, slide valves.

A centre engine is a semi-portable overtype engine built into the truck carrying the centre assembly of a fairground 'ride'. Engines were twin cylinder, to ensure positive starting. This particular engine came from a set of three-abreast gallopers. Drive from the engine was to a main gear or 'cheese wheel' which gave rotating motion to the roundabout and also operated a series of radial three-throw crankshafts which imparted the galloping action to the animals on the ride.

On top of the smokebox is a single cylinder inverted vertical engine, often known as the model, which drove the organ, at one time an essential part of any ride. The flue is taken from the bottom of the smokebox and was led by a side connection to the centre pole of the roundabout which was hollow and acted as the chimney. Other fittings on the engine are the diagonal boiler feed-pump driven by an eccentric on the end of the crankshaft, an injector and a steam water-lifter. This was used to transfer water from a water cart to the engine's tank. A set of whistles to attract customers and make the girls scream was also an essential feature. Also in the Thursford Collection is a similar centre engine mounted in a set of Venetian Gondolas.

SINGLE CYLINDER HORIZONTAL ENGINES
FROM NORWICH GAS WORKS
Marshall, Sons & Co Ltd, Gainsborough, slide valve, 7 hp.
Tilghman & Co Ltd, air compressing engine.

Both of these engines are run under steam from time to time supplied from one of the traction engines. Although they built considerable numbers of steam-driven air-compressors Tilghman & Co appear to be represented in preservation only by this small engine.

ULSTER MUSEUM Botanic Gardens, Belfast
The opening of a Hall of Engineering has enabled three stationary engines to be displayed, and in an excellent manner too, together with the front section of a Lancashire boiler. Belfast was an important centre for the manufacture of engines for the Ulster linen trade.

INVERTED VERTICAL COMPOUND MILL ENGINE
FROM FALLS FLAX SPINNING Co, BELFAST
Victor Coates & Co Ltd, Belfast, 1898. 18 in (HP), 32 in (LP) × 36 in stroke. Corliss valves, Dobson's trip gear, Porter type governor, flywheel 12 ft diameter, grooved for ten ropes, 400 hp, 101 rpm 100 psi, single-cylinder inverted-vertical barring engine.

The engines used in the Ulster linen trade were generally similar to the engines of the cotton and woollen industries of Lancashire and Yorkshire. Victor Coates exported a few engines to England, but this trade was small and Ulster was the main home outlet. The firm closed in 1906. The engine here is of substantial construction with heavy columns supporting the cylinders and the flywheel boarded in with pine boarding. The condenser is below floor level at the rear of the engine with the air pump driven by a rocking lever from the HP crosshead.

SINGLE CYLINDER HORIZONTAL MILL ENGINE
FROM DRAPERSFIELD, CO DERRY
Victor Coates & Co Ltd, Belfast, 1895, 15 in × 24 in, Corliss valves, Dobson's trip gear, Porter type governor, flywheel grooved for seven ropes, 9 ft diameter, 80 hp, 100 psi.

This engine was first used to supply electric lighting to the Belfast Art and Industry Exhibition held in the White Linen Hall, where it operated as a non condensing engine driving a generator supplying about 700 lights. Following the exhibition it was taken by traction engine and trailer to Drapersfield and it apparently slipped off the wagon while en route. At Drapersfield a condenser was fitted and the engine supplemented the power from water turbines to drive a weaving mill. It worked until about 1950. At the Ulster Museum the engine is demonstrated at 16 rpm (about one fifth of working speed) by an electric motor drive.

SINGLE CYLINDER HORIZONTAL MILL
ENGINE
FROM ULSTER WOOLLEN MILLS, CRUMLIN,
CO ANTRIM
John Rowan & Sons Ltd, Belfast, 1876, 24 in ×
36 in, drop valves, Rowan's cut-off gear, Watt
type governor, flywheel 16 ft 3 in diameter
grooved for three ropes, c50 hp, 70 rpm.

The last surviving engine of this maker in
Ulster, it worked for nearly 80 years. The drop
valves are placed in chests or nozzles at the side
of the cylinder and are operated by cams driven
by side shaft and bevel gearing from the
crankshaft. The cut-off gear was patented by
John Rowan in 1848. The piston has a tail rod
supported on slides. The condenser was below
the floor in front of the cylinder with the air
pump driven by a rocker arm. For demonstration purposes an electric motor now drives
the engine at 4 rpm.

*Welsh Industrial & Maritime Museum. The
later Walker colliery fan engines closely re-
sembled textile mill engines although the four-
cylinder triple expansion layout was unusual for a
fan engine, cross-compound being normal. This
fan engine has governor controlled trip gear on the
inlet Corliss valves of the HP and IP cylinders.
The trip gear on the two tandem LP cylinders is
hand adjusted.*

**WELSH INDUSTRIAL AND MARITIME
MUSEUM,** Bute Street Docks, Cardiff
A section of the National Museum of Wales
(Amgueddfa Genedlaethol Cymru), this
museum houses an important collection of
engines. The museum holds a large triple-
expansion inverted-vertical waterworks pumping engine from Elkesley, Notts (not yet re-
erected), and one of the Bull pumping engines
from the Severn Tunnel Sudbrook pumping
station. This is one of only three survivors —
the others being an engine still in situ at Kew
Bridge, and the second engine from Sudbrook
which is now held by the Science Museum,
South Kensington.

TWIN TANDEM TRIPLE EXPANSION FAN
ENGINE
FROM CRUMLIN NAVIGATION COLLIERY,
GWENT
Walker Bros, Pagefield Ironworks, Wigan,
1911, 15 in (HP), 23½ in (IP), (2) 26 in (LP), ×
39 in stroke, Corliss valves, Dobson's trip gear,
Porter governor, trunk crosshead guides, fly-
wheel 15 ft diameter grooved for fourteen
ropes, 500 hp, 60 rpm, 160 psi.

This extremely important exhibit is one of the
very few mine ventilating fan engines to
survive, and is the only one of the once
numerous Walker engines to be preserved.

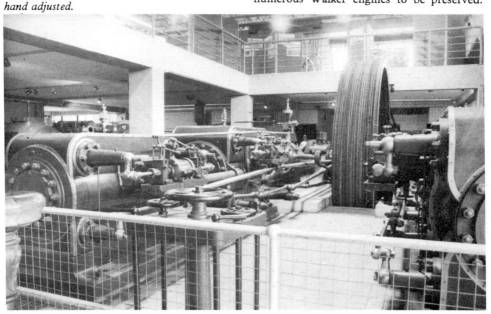

Walker Brothers were in the forefront of mine ventilation and supplied hundreds of their backward-curved blade centrifugal-fans together with the engines to drive them. The fans were very strongly made (Walker's brand name was 'Indestructible'), and so were the engines for they had to run for very long periods without stopping. Such was their reliability that it was unusual to find stand-by plant where Walker engines and fans were installed. The Crumlin Navigation engine drove an 'Indestructible' fan 24 ft diameter by 8 ft wide, which was capable of circulating 300,000 cubic feet of air per minute through the underground workings. The engine is extremely heavily built for its power, which ensured long and reliable running.

SINGLE CYLINDER INVERTED VERTICAL
ENCLOSED MINE FAN ENGINE
FROM ABERBEEG SOUTH COLLIERY, GWENT
E. Reader & Sons, Nottingham, 1924, piston valve, self lubricating, 150 rpm.

During the twentieth century centrifugal fans with forward-curved blades came into use for mine ventilation, although they in no way ousted the large Walker-type fans. Running at much higher speed than the 100 rpm or thereabouts of the backward-bladed fans the forward-blade type were often direct coupled to high-speed enclosed engines. The Aberbeeg engine is a small one of its type and drove a 6 ft diameter 'Keith' fan.

Welsh Industrial & Maritime Museum. This Tangye engine is typical of thousands made for small and medium power requirements.

SINGLE CYLINDER HORIZONTAL ENGINE &
DIRECT CURRENT GENERATOR
FROM BARRY URBAN DISTRICT COUNCIL
REFUSE DESTRUCTOR
Messrs Tangye, Birmingham, c1900, 10 in × 20 in, slide valve, Pickering governor, girder bed, trunk crosshead guide, disc crank. Wilson Hartnell belt-driven 110 volt DC generator.

The late Victorians and Edwardians were more energy conscious than is generally realised today. In common with many other local authorities, Barry burnt the town's refuse in destructor furnaces and used the heat to raise steam, in this case in a Babcock & Wilcox water-tube boiler. At Barry the steam was used to power the Tangye engine and a mortar mill (now displayed outside the museum). The electricity generated by the engine and generator supplied the destructor works buildings and a nearby school. The mortar mill ground down the residual ashes and clinker from the destructor furnaces for use in road making around the town.

HORIZONTAL SINGLE CYLINDER ENGINE
FROM LLANTWIT MAJOR SAWMILL
SOUTH GLAMORGAN
Alexander & Co, Newport, 1865, rebuilt by Baker & Co, Albion Works, East Moors, Cardiff 1895. 7½ in × 14 in, slide valve, throttle governor, four-bar crosshead guides, disc crank, marine type big-end, wood-lagged cylinder, flywheel 5 ft diameter, 15 hp.

A small engine of very simple design latterly used to drive a generator. Engines of this type were built in large numbers by small engineering firms all over Britain to fulfil local requirements for power.

INVERTED VERTICAL TANDEM COMPOUND
HIGH SPEED ENCLOSED ENGINE &
DYNAMOMETER
FROM UNIVERSITY OF WALES, CARDIFF
Belliss & Morcom, Birmingham, 250-350 rpm, 8·4 kW.

A small engine coupled to a direct current generator used as a dynamometer for experimental purposes and instruction in the engineering laboratories.

Welsh Industrial & Maritime Museum. Although rebuilt by Baker & Co, East Moors, in 1885 this horizontal engine from Llantwit Major sawmill retains the character of its original building date, 1865.

Welsh Industrial & Maritime Museum. Belliss & Morcom high speed engine from Bland's woodyard. Note the small generator or exciter on the end of the generator shaft.

INVERTED VERTICAL HIGH SPEED ENCLOSED
COMPOUND ENGINE & ALTERNATOR
FROM JOHN BLAND'S TIMBERYARD, CARDIFF
Belliss & Morcom, Birmingham, 1910, 14½ in
(HP), 21 in (LP) × 10 in stroke, piston valves,
428 rpm, 100 psi. Mather & Platt 120 kW
direct-coupled alternator.

First used at Grange Colliery, Staffordshire, this engine was moved to the timber yard in 1928, where it provided lighting and power for wood-working machinery. This type of engine was very popular in industry and in public services where the exhaust steam could be used for other purposes, such as heating, providing hot water etc. Similar engines are still made today by Belliss & Morcom.

TABLE ENGINE
FROM CADOXTON BREWERY, NEATH
Neath Abbey Iron Co, 5¾ in × 20 in.

Introduced by Henry Maudslay in 1807, the table engine was designed to meet small power requirements and dispensed with the beam. The design kept the crankshaft as low as possible while using a vertical cylinder.

Welsh Industrial & Maritime Museum. The Cadoxton Brewery table engine with the cylinder sitting on its table.

Welsh Industrial & Maritime Museum. Single-column rotative beam pumping engine from Llanishen Waterworks. Made by Harvey of Hayle in 1851.

SINGLE COLUMN ROTATIVE BEAM PUMPING ENGINE
FROM CARDIFF WATERWORKS COMPANY, LLANISHEN RESERVOIR

Harvey & Co, Hayle, Cornwall, 1851, 20 in × 42 in, slide valve, single plate cast-iron beam, Watt-type governor, flywheel 12 ft diameter, 20 hp, 30 rpm.

The single column of Grecian style was much used in smaller beam engines to support the beam trunnions. This engine was built by a famous firm of Cornish engineers and designed by James Simpson, later to become pre-eminent in the world of pumps.

TWIN CYLINDER INVERTED VERTICAL PUMP FROM LLANHARRY IRON ORE MINE, GLAMORGAN

This type of pump with 'banjo' pump rod inside which the connecting rod and crank rotated, was very widely used for all kinds of pumping duties. It could be worked on steam, or if placed underground, on compressed air. Each side drove a single acting ram pump, and the cranks were set at 180 degrees. Often known as 'Cameron' pumps, many were made by John Cameron of Manchester.

SINGLE CYLINDER HORIZONTAL BANJO PUMP
FROM MONMOUTH GASWORKS

Joseph Evans, Wolverhampton.

A type of pump extensively used in gasworks for pumping by-products. They would run for long periods with little attention, often in atrocious environmental conditions.

DIRECT ACTING SINGLE CYLINDER INVERTED VERTICAL PUMP FROM NEWPORT TUBE WORKS

G. & J. Weir, Cathcart, Glasgow

Universally used for supplying boiler feed water, this pattern of pump had an ingenious valve operated from the piston rod. The valve gear operated a small slide valve which alternately admitted steam to each end of a 'shuttle'. The shuttle was blown from side to side and worked the main valve, which admitted and exhausted steam to and from the cylinder.

DIRECT ACTING HORIZONTAL CEMENTATION PUMP
FROM GLAMORGAN COLLIERY, LLWYNPIA
Joseph Evans, Wolverhampton.

To enable shaft sinking to be carried out safely through fragmented rock, cement is injected into the strata at high pressure to bind the rock together and also to form a barrier against the ingress of water. Working on compressed air this pump could deliver cement at 3,000 psi.

SINGLE CYLINDER A-FRAME VERTICAL ENGINE
FROM NIXON'S NAVIGATION COLLIERY, MOUNTAIN ASH, GLAMORGAN

The vertical engine was the first design breakaway from the beam engine for mill driving, and could be made in very small sizes and self contained. This small engine was used to drive a pump.

SINGLE CYLINDER HORIZONTAL GEARED HAULAGE ENGINE
FROM PARK COLLIERY, CWMPARC, RHONDDA FAWR
Llewellyn & Cubitt, Pentre, c1870, 16 in × 36 in, slide valve, Stephenson's link motion, flywheel 11 ft diameter, geared winding drum 4 ft diameter.

Welsh Industrial & Maritime Museum. Old type of colliery haulage engine with single cylinder and geared rope drum. Made in the Rhondda by Llewellyn & Cubitt.

Haulage engines with geared winding drums were found in large numbers above and below ground at collieries. Mostly they were twin cylinder, but the older ones often had a single cylinder only. Underground engines at first worked on steam, either from boilers placed near the shaft bottom or piped down the shaft from the surface boilers. Later compressed air was used. This engine worked above ground hauling trams of colliery waste up an incline for tipping on the mountain sides.

TURBO-ALTERNATOR
FROM HATFIELD MAIN COLLIERY, YORKSHIRE
British Thomson-Houston, Rugby, 1925, 3,000 rpm, 329 amps at 3,300 volts, 140 psi.

The turbine was patented by Parsons in 1884, and was made in ever larger sizes, eventually completely replacing the reciprocating engine where high power was required. Basically steam from a series of nozzles impinges on blades carried on a disc fixed to a shaft. The nozzles cause the steam to move at high velocity and this in turn makes the turbine

Welsh Industrial & Maritime Museum. British Thomson Houston turbo-alternator set of about 2,000 horse power. Compare the size with the 500 hp Walker fan engine.

shaft rotate at high speed. The steam is expanded through a series of blade discs or 'stages' mounted along the shaft. This turbine set is small by present-day standards and the working pressure is a tenth of that used in modern power stations. Although this set used steam direct from the boilers, it was quite common at collieries to use mixed-pressure turbines. Exhaust steam from winding engines was admitted at a low pressure stage of the turbine, which reduced the intake of steam direct from the boilers.

WENDRON FORGE, Helston, Cornwall

The Wendron Forge Museum was established around a blacksmith's shop and contains many and varied industrial exhibits including a large number of stationary steam engines. The engines are outdoors and are operated by compressed air. The museum also incorporates the adjacent Wheal Roots tin mine.

CORNISH PUMPING ENGINE
FROM GREENSPLAT CLAYWORKS
Maker unknown, c1850, 30 in × 9 ft × 8 ft, twin plate cast-iron beam, twin plug rods, single perpendicular pipe, single cataract.

Built as a rotative engine, this engine was obtained from Bunny Mine in 1894 for £65 as the Greensplat Clayworks required a flywheel. The other parts lay in the open for a year or two, then in 1897 the engine was re-erected as a pumping engine to pump clay slurry. Pumping depth was 240 ft and 500 gpm were raised. The engine worked until 1959 and was the last Cornish pumping engine to work in Cornwall. It was re-erected at Wendron Forge 1972-3. As the engine is out-doors it is possible to stand back and see it in its entirety.

The narrow beam of the engine with the parallel motion loops outside the beam plates indicates that it may have been built outside Cornwall, possibly in Devon.

Wendron Forge. 30 inch Cornish pumping engine from Greensplat Clayworks. Note the shear legs with pulley for lifting and lowering 'pitwork', ie pump and pump rods, in the shaft.

Wendron Forge. Tandem compound gas exhauster engine made by Waller of Stroud. Construction is extremely heavy with large bearing surfaces on crankshaft and crank.

TANDEM COMPOUND HORIZONTAL ENGINE
FROM PINKNEY'S GREEN BRICKWORKS,
MAIDENHEAD
Thomas Metcalfe, Bradford, c1888, 12 in (HP) x 18 in (LP) ×24 in stroke, slide valves, 120 hp, 100 rpm.

A very simple engine used for driving brickworks machinery. No condenser was fitted, the exhaust steam being used to heat the drying floors for the 'green' bricks before they were put into the kilns. The engine runs 'under', ie the connecting rod goes under the crank on the outward stroke. This would be to suit the disposition of machinery drives in the brickworks.

TANDEM COMPOUND HORIZONTAL ENGINE
FROM CROYDON GASWORKS
G. Waller & Sons, Stroud

Waller's specialised in gasworks machinery and their engines were built to run for long periods without stopping. This engine has a double web crank with crankshaft bearings each side.

Wendron Forge. Twin cylinder mine haulage engine with geared drum made by Holman Bros Camborne. Compare with the single cylinder engine in the Welsh Industrial & Maritime Museum.

SINGLE CYLINDER HORIZONTAL ENGINE FROM HELSTON WORKHOUSE LAUNDRY
J.J. Lane, London, c1910.

Lane's specialised in completely equipping laundries. In the days before individual electric motor drives, a steam engine was often supplied to drive the machinery.

TWIN CYLINDER MINE HAULAGE ENGINE
Holman Bros, Camborne, 1905, 10 in × 13 in, slide valves, Stephenson's valve gear, twin rope drums.

Engines of this type were used for hauling minerals by wire rope at surface and under-ground. They were also used as winding engines at the shafts of small mines and at the subsidiary shafts of large mines. The twin rope drums with clutched connection enabled bal-anced winding to take place from various levels, or the drums could be operated in-dependently. Many of these engines worked on compressed air. The whole engine could be broken down into components small enough to be lowered down a mine shaft for erection underground.

TWIN CYLINDER DIAGONAL MINE HAULAGE ENGINE
FROM SOUTH CROFTY MINE, CAMBORNE
Holman Bros, Camborne.

Engines like this with a geared winding drum could be found dotted around underground in any large mine. The diagonal arrangement saved space but horizontal engines were very common. They ran equally well on steam or compressed air.

SINGLE CYLINDER INVERTED VERTICAL ENGINE
George Waller & Son, Stroud.

A very simple engine of massive construction for driving gasworks machinery.

TRIPLE EXPANSION HIGH SPEED INVERTED VERTICAL ENCLOSED ENGINE
FROM NEWTON ABBOT POWER STATION
Belliss & Morcom Ltd, Birmingham

High speed engines such as this, directly coupled to electrical generators were widely used in the early days of public electricity supply. Quickly outclassed by increasing pub-lic demand for electricity necessitating the use of turbines, the type remained popular for providing private supply in isolated locations. Some remained in use at power stations power-ing auxiliary plant.

Wendron Forge. Single cylinder high speed engine by Reader of Nottingham, direct coupled to a gas compressor. Was used at the ICI works at Billingham.

INVERTED VERTICAL ENGINE
FROM WINCHESTER REFUSE DESTRUCTOR
S. S. Stott & Co, Haslingden, Lancs.

Well known in Lancashire as makers of mill engines, Stotts made, and still do, machinery for municipal refuse and sewage works. This engine was supplied to drive this type of plant.

BANJO PUMPS
Cameron-type pump by Joseph Evans & Co, Wolverhampton, c1910, used to pump tar in a gasworks.
Pearn-type pump by Frank Pearn & Co, Manchester, c1900, used to pump water.

Banjo pumps were made in two general forms. One type had a 'banjo' shaped pump rod with a connecting rod turning a crank inside the banjo. A heavy flywheel on the crankshaft ensured steady running. This form of pump was often called 'Cameron' in the north of England but was in fact made by a variety of builders.

The second type of pump had a banjo shaped connecting rod which encompassed the pump barrel and turned a crankshaft at the bottom of the machine. This type of pump in small sizes was often bolted to a wall. They were often known as 'Mumford' or 'Pearn' pumps.

Both types of pump were used for pumping water, tar, or any other liquid. Cameron type pumps certainly were used for public water supply where demand was small.

HIGH SPEED INVERTED VERTICAL ENCLOSED ENGINES
Compound engine and generator by Ashworth & Parker, Bury, Lancs, 1927 — used for electric lighting at Kempton pumping station.
Compound engine by E. Reader & Co, Nottingham, c1930 — Machinery drive by belts at ICI Billingham works.
Single cylinder engine and gas compressor, by E. Reader & Co, c1930, used at ICI Billingham.
Single cylinder engine by E. Reader & Co, Nottingham, c1930, used to drive machinery at Paddington Technical College.
Belliss & Morcom engine and asphalt pump – worked at a remote location at the end of a long steam line, pumping asphalt in an oil refinery.

DIRECT ACTING PUMPS
Vertical direct acting pump, G. & J. Weir, 1916, supplied boiler feed water at Elba Steel Works, Gowerton, South Wales.
Vertical direct acting pump, G. & J. Weir, c1918, supplied fuel oil to oil fired boilers at Elba Steel Works.
Horizontal 'Duplex' pump by Joseph Evans, Wolverhampton.

High speed engines were made in a wide variety of sizes for powering generators air compressors and also for driving miscellaneous machinery by belts. Wendron has a number of these interesting engines which were capable of running for months with little attention. Some of these have been described above and here are brief details of the smaller engines in the collection.

A multitude of direct-acting pumps were for auxiliary services such as boiler feeding. Steam pistons were coupled directly to the water ram or piston by a common rod. Familiar

Wendron Forge. Single cylinder or 'Simplex' direct acting boiler feed pump by G. & J. Weir.

names were Weir of Glasgow, and Worthington-Simpson of Newark-on-Trent.

INVERTED VERTICAL COMPOUND ENGINE
Sisson's of Gloucester, 1954.

Many engines of this type were supplied to colleges (this one was at Paddington Technical College) for training students in the theory and practice of thermo-dynamics. The engine could be run as a compound, or each side separately with permutations of cut-off and direction of rotation. Power output was measured by brake gear on the flywheel.

Access to the Museum is daily April-October.

WORTLEY TOP FORGE,
Thurgoland, South Yorkshire
This site is a former forge dating back to the seventeenth century. A large amount of water-driven forge plant has been assembled together with several steam engines from various sources. These are now run under steam from time to time. The engines described here are stationary engines, but there are also steam launch engines and a lawn mower engine.

SINGLE CYLINDER VERTICAL ENGINE
FROM NEEPSEND GASWORKS
Maker unknown, c1852, 14 in × 30 in.

This engine drove the mortar mill at the gasworks, mortar being in demand where old coke ovens were in use, as they had the fronts bricked up after charging with coal. Re-erection has been carried out in a simulated engine house as this engine like many of its type is 'house built'.

SINGLE CYLINDER HORIZONTAL ENGINE
FROM A SAW MILL, BASLOW, DERBYSHIRE
Buxton & Thornley, Burton-on-Trent, c1885, 10 in × 14 in, slide valve, Porter governor.

An engine typical of thousands made to perform mundane tasks. The bed-stones of this engine are part of an old cheese press, illustrating how useful items were often re-used for totally different purposes

SINGLE CYLINDER INVERTED VERTICAL ENGINE
Wells of Sheffield, 1888, 3½ in × 5 in.

A tiny engine which indicates just how small working steam engines were made before the advent of the electric motor.

INVERTED VERTICAL COMPOUND ENGINE
FROM ROTHERHAM TECHNICAL COLLEGE
Marshall, Sons & Co, Ltd, Gainsborough, 1930s, 4½ in (HP), 7½ in (LP) × 10 in stroke, Meyer expansion slide valve HP, Stephenson's link motion LP, fitted with dynamometer brake.

Most technical colleges at one time had specially designed steam engines to instruct students in the theory and practice of thermo-dynamics. HP and LP sides could be run together, or one at a time, etc, and the exhaust could be condensed or turned to atmosphere as desired. The condenser and air pump on this engine have been removed.

INVERTED VERTICAL COMPOUND HIGH SPEED ENCLOSED ENGINE
FROM HEATH HOUSE MILL, GOLCAR
Browett, Lindley & Co Ltd, Patricroft, 1915, 120 hp, 500 rpm.

Many engines of this type were supplied to factories, collieries etc for the generation of electrical power before the 'grid' was developed and with it universal electric power.

SINGLE CYLINDER INVERTED VERTICAL
HIGH SPEED ENCLOSED ENGINE
Sissons of Gloucester, 1930s, 4 in × 5 in, piston valve.

Large numbers of these small enclosed engines were made by this and other makers. They were put to a variety of uses, eg driving small electrical power generators, fans and centrifugal pumps.

TWIN CYLINDER CAMERON PUMP
FROM SANDERSON, KAYSER LTD,
SHEFFIELD
Maker unknown, c1913, 8 in × 8 in.

The duty of this pump was to pump water from the River Don for works services.

VERTICAL SIMPLEX BOILER FEED PUMP
FROM ROYAL NAVY, & PARKGATE IRON &
STEEL WORKS
G. & J. Weir Ltd, Cathcart, pre-1914, 5 in × 10 in.

This pump was originally fitted in a warship and saw naval service throughout World War I. Later it was used at Parkgate where it served until 1975. It is typical of the smaller sizes in the range of 'Weir' pumps.

PORTABLE STEAM PUMP
FROM ROYAL NAVY
Shand, Mason Ltd, 4 in × 4 in

Made by a firm at one time famous for the manufacture of steam fire engines, the purpose of this pump was to be taken ashore in remote places and pump fresh water out to the ship. It was allocated originally to a 'Valiant' class destroyer.

INVERTED VERTICAL TWIN CYLINDER
BARRING ENGINE
FROM ELKESLEY WATERWORKS, RETFORD,
NOTTS
Ashton, Frost, Blackburn, 1911.

Large steam engines usually had a small barring engine, which could be engaged with a toothed ring on the flywheel, to turn the engine for maintenance purposes or to a correct position for starting. This engine served a large inverted-vertical triple-expansion pumping engine.

VERTICAL CROSS-TUBE BOILER
Lumby & Co, Halifax, 1949, 3 ft diameter × 8 ft high, three cross water-tubes, evaporation rate 300 lb per hour (approx).

Thousands of these boilers were made for use in any location where a small supply of steam was required, eg small clothing factories for running the garment press, dairies, pig farms and building sites, etc. Efficiency was low, with much heat going straight up the chimney. The water tubes placed across the upper part of the firebox helped to absorb a little more heat as it rushed towards the exit. Before the days of the present stringent safety regulations these boilers were often sorely abused.

3 ON SITE PRESERVATION
Access on Open Days

BANCROFT SHED, Barnoldswick, Lancs

CROSS COMPOUND HORIZONTAL MILL ENGINE

William Roberts & Sons Ltd, Phoenix Foundry, Nelson, 1922. 18in (HP), 36in (LP) × 48in stroke, Corliss valves, governor controlled trip gear HP, hand adjusted trip gear LP, jet condenser below floor, LP tail rod drive to air pump through rocker arm, thirteen rope drive to mill shaft, inverted vertical twin cylinder barring engine, 600ihp, 68rpm, 160psi. One Lancashire boiler 160psi, fitted with J. Proctor's wide ram coking stokers, One Cornish boiler 80psi, hand fired.

Formerly in the West Riding of Yorkshire, Barnoldswick's ('Barlick' in local vernacular) Bancroft Shed was one of the few cotton weaving mills in that county, but its engine was made just over the border in Lancashire. William Roberts & Sons, were well known in East Lancashire and this engine is typical of their late engines. The weaving shed had 1,000 looms and the engine, always immaculately kept, gave good service until the mill closed in 1978. The Lancashire boiler provided steam for the engine, while the Cornish boiler which has an off-set furnace tube, was installed to supply steam for taping frames and space heating. In fact it was little used, the Lancashire generally carrying the whole load.

The Bancroft engine is in the care of the Bancroft Mill Engine Trust and is the latest of stationary engine preservation schemes to come into being. Access is on open days and the engine will be in steam.

Bancroft Shed. The valve gear on the LP cylinder is simpler than on the HP as the trips are hand adjusted. The nameplate says Mary Jane; the HP engine is called James.

95

ASTLEY GREEN COLLIERY, Leigh, Lancs

TWIN TANDEM COMPOUND COLLIERY
WINDING ENGINE
Yates & Thom Ltd, Blackburn, 1912, 35 in
(HP), 60 in (LP) × 72 in stroke, Corliss valves,
governor controlled trip gear, Allan's straight
link valve-gear, bi-cylindro-conical drum
16 ft 8 in to 27 ft diameter, post brakes,
Worsley Mesnes brake and reversing engines,
Metrovick controller, maximum rope speed
80 ft/sec, 205 tons/hour from 873 yd, superheated steam 160 psi, 3,300 hp.

Built for the new Astley Green Colliery in
1912, this was the largest winding engine in
Lancashire and one of the largest in Britain.
The engine house and headgear are the only
structures now remaining on the site, as the
colliery closed in 1970. When in operation the
plant at the colliery was most impressive. A
Yates & Thom cross-compound winding
engine served the second shaft, a large Walker
cross-compound drove the ventilating fan, and
there was a range of turbine-driven generators
and air compressors. Sixteen Lancashire boilers in one bank, with Green's economisers and
Sugden superheaters, provided the steam.

The engine is being restored and may be
visited on most summer Sunday afternoons.
Other engines are also being collected here.

*Astley Green Colliery. Cylinders and Corliss
valve gear of one side of the twin tandem
compound engine. Both HP and LP trip gears are
linked to a governor which shortened the cut-off
as speed increased.*

CARBOLITE FURNACES LTD,
Bamford Mill, Derbys

TANDEM COMPOUND MILL ENGINE
John Musgrave & Sons Ltd, Bolton, 1907,
16 in (HP), 30 in (LP) × 30 in stroke, piston
drop valves, trunk crosshead guides, boarded
flywheel grooved for fourteen ropes, 450 hp,
103 rpm, twin-cylinder vertical barring engine.
Two Galloway boilers, 1929, Neil's furnaces,
superheaters, Green's economisers, 165 psi,
550°F.

Continental manufacturers at the beginning of
the twentieth century were producing very
economical engines having drop valves and
using superheated steam. Inroads were even
made into supplying engines for the Lancashire textile mills. British engine builders were
quick to follow suit, in some cases engaging
Continental designers. Drop valves took two
forms, the old Cornish type with double
seats — the 'double-beat valve' — or the piston
drop valve where a small piston uncovered and
closed ports in a sleeve as it rose and fell. Some
large Continental engines had four seated
valves. Double and multiple-seat valves need
very careful fitting, under steam, to get them
right, and were noisy as the valve dropped on
to its seat. Piston drop valves were much easier
to fit and there was less noise and wear.

The Bamford engine is very Continental in
appearance, neat but of extremely strong construction. The valves are fitted in the cylinder
end covers to keep clearance volume to the
absolute minimum. Drive to the valves is by
eccentrics and short rods from a layshaft bevel
geared to the crankshaft. Trip gear is fitted to
the inlet valves of both cylinders, the HP trip
gear being governor controlled. The HP cylinder is behind the LP and typical Musgrave
features are the underfloor condenser with air
pump driven from the crosshead, boarded
flywheel with the boards splayed out to meet
the rim and the old type vertical barring
engine.

Bamford mill occupies a very old site being
originally a water powered flour mill. Textiles
came later. The mill closed in 1963 and was
taken over in 1965 for the manufacture of
electric furnaces. The engine was not needed
but has been maintained in working order by
the present owner. Access is on open days
when the engine is run under steam and at
other times by application. Details should be
obtained from the mill at Bamford, near
Sheffield.

*Bamford Mill. With the introduction of drop
valves the 'Continental Look' was adopted by
many British manufacturers. The strong construction combined with piston drop valves made
this Musgrave tandem a robust, quiet and
economical engine.*

CHEDDAR'S LANE SEWAGE WORKS, Cambridge

TANDEM COMPOUND DIFFERENTIAL PUMPING ENGINE
Hathorn, Davey, Sun Foundry, Leeds, 1894, 22 in (HP), 44 in (LP) × 48 in stroke, Meyer expansion slide valves, differential valve gear, 14 spm. Three Babcock & Wilcox water tube boilers, Manlove Alliot destructor furnaces; one Babcock & Wilcox water tube boiler, coke fired, 90 psi.

The Davey differential pumping engine was a scientific approach to the reciprocating pump. The aim was to provide an equal effort at the pump rams throughout the stroke. With a normal pump the effort varies, as the thrust on the steam pistons is far from constant. To obtain equal effort at the pumps Davey coupled the piston rod to a rocking wheel. To other points on this wheel the pump rods were attached. The points of attachment were chosen so that the pump rams moved at maximum speed when the steam piston thrust was greatest, and vice versa. Loss of load on a non-rotative pump can be disastrous, and in Davey's differential valve-gear the valve was operated by a combination of linkage from the piston rod and a small steam engine, whose speed was controlled by a cataract. Any tendency to overspeed overtook the valve-gear engine and steam was cut off. In extreme cases steam would be admitted to the opposite side of the piston to arrest its motion.

Steam raising was initially by the three water tube boilers heated by the destructor furnaces. In course of time the combustible content of domestic refuse decreased and a supplementary coke fired boiler was installed in 1932. If necessary the destructor boilers could also be fired on coke, a grate being fitted which could be fired from the operating floor. Later the steam pumps were supplemented by two single-cylinder horizontal National gas engines, each driving a Gwynnes centrifugal pump by flat belt.

The plant auxiliaries are interesting. Electric lighting was supplied by a 2 kW, 110 volt DC generator direct coupled to a Bumpstead & Chandler single-cylinder high-speed enclosed inverted-vertical engine. A Mumford 'banjo' pump supplied boiler-feed water. There are also two Worthington Simpson horizontal duplex steam pumps which circulated cooling water for the gas engines.

The whole plant ceased work in 1968, but the site was taken over by Cambridge City Museums. Some of the destructor boilers have been demolished, but eventually the coke fired boiler will supply steam to run the engines light. Access is on public open days, details obtainable from Cambridge City Museums.

Cheddar's Lane. Tandem compound differential pumping engine. The point of attachment of one of the pump rods can just be discerned.

COMBE SAWMILL,
Blenheim Estate, Oxfordshire

FOUR COLUMN SINGLE BEAM ENGINE
Thomas Piggott, Birmingham, 1852, 18 in ×
34 in, slide valve, gab valve-gear, Watt type
governor, single-plate cast-iron beam, flywheel 13 ft 6 in diameter. Cornish boiler, Thos
Piggott, 1852, 5 ft × 19 ft, 50 psi.

Beam engines for small powers were often
made self contained on a bed-plate with the
beam trunnions supported by one or more
cast-iron columns. This engine was installed to
assist a 13 ft × 8 ft waterwheel and may have
been a fairly standard design of the makers.
Registers are provided on the bedplate for
bearing pedestals to suit right- and left-hand
engines.

The Combe engine is very plain with the
entablature on which the beam trunnions are
mounted supported under the beam centre by
four inclined cast-iron columns, with additional support by a small column fixed to the
cylinder. The entablature also carries the
parallel-motion linkage. Below the bedplate is
the condenser and air pump located indoors of
the beam centre. The boiler feed-pump and
condenser cooling-water pump are outdoors of
the beam centre. All are worked by rods from
the beam, the air pump rod being guided by
parallel motion. The connecting rod is the
original cast-iron cruciform cross section.
Drive to the mill is by belts from a countershaft carrying a pinion which engages with the
toothed rim of the flywheel.

Steam is still provided by the Cornish boiler
although pressure is now reduced to 20 psi. It
must qualify as one of the oldest working
boilers in the world. The steam plant was last
used in 1912, but with the blessing of the Duke
of Marlborough restoration began in 1969 and
the engine ran once more in 1974. Access is on
open days and details are obtainable from the
Hon Secretary, Combe Mill Society, 18 The
Slade, Charlbury, Oxon.

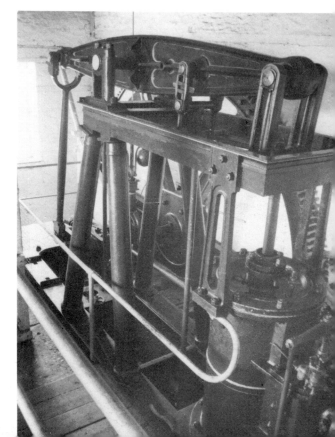

*Combe Sawmill. The four-column
design was an alternative to the
A-frame for small beam engines.
This engine of 1852 shows none of
the decoration found on many
contemporary engines and is
strictly functional.*

DEE MILL, Shaw, Oldham, Lancs

TWIN TANDEM COMPOUND MILL ENGINE
Scott & Hodgson, Guide Bridge, 1907, 18½ in
(HP), 44 in (LP) × 60 in stroke. Corliss valves
HP, piston valves LP, Lumb's governor, flywheel 26 ft diameter grooved for thirty-eight
ropes, 1,500 hp, 60 rpm, 200 psi. Twin cylinder inverted-vertical barring engine.

The Dee engine represents Lancashire engineering at its zenith. A few makers used
piston valves on low pressure cylinders and
Scott & Hodgson were one of these. On some
of their large inverted vertical triple expansion
engines they fitted *two* piston valves to the LP
cylinder. The piston valves on this engine are
driven by eccentrics and rods from the crankshaft. The Corliss valves take their motion
from a cross-shaft behind the LP cylinders
which is driven through a layshaft and bevel
gears from the crankshaft. Scott & Hodgson
Corliss valve trip gear required three eccentrics to operate if one includes the drive to
the exhaust valves. As the engine has two HP
cylinders six eccentrics are mounted on the
cross-shaft. Each LP cylinder has its own
condenser and these are located below the

floor. The air pumps are driven by rocker arms
coupled to the crossheads. The flywheel is
boarded as was common on large engines to
eliminate the fan effect of the whirling spokes.

The engine ceased work in 1968 and the
owners allowed it to remain in situ, probably
the best way to preserve a stationary engine as
it is seen in its working surroundings.

*Dee Mill. Spinning mill engines represented
Lancashire (and Cheshire) engine building at its
zenith. The Dee twin tandem is typical in
general, but all were different in detail.*

Dee Mill. From whatever angle the Dee engine is viewed it is impressive. Note that the big-end lubrication is force feed and does not depend on centrifugal action.

Dee Mill. On big engines a barring engine was essential. Scott & Hodgson used a neat twin-cylinder inverted vertical design.

DIAMOND WORKS, Royton, Oldham, Lancs

INVERTED VERTICAL COMPOUND MILL
ENGINE
Scott & Hodgson, Guide Bridge, 1912, named
Lily, 14 in (HP), 30 in (LP) × 30 in stroke,
Corliss valves HP, piston valve LP, flywheel
grooved for fourteen ropes, 250 hp, 90 rpm.
Lancashire boiler by Tinker, Shenton, oil
fired, 140 psi.

Few inverted-vertical mill engines have
survived and this is an excellent example of
medium powered engines in general, and Scott
& Hodgson practice in particular. The cylinders are each carried on very substantial cast-
iron columns rigidly tied together just below
cylinder level to make, in conjunction with the
bedplate, a very strong frame. Behind the LP
cylinder columns is the condenser air-pump

and the boiler feed-pump driven by a twin-
plate rocking-beam from the LP crosshead.
The Corliss valve trip gear is Scott &
Hodgson's patent and cut-off control is by a
Lumb's governor. Drive was taken from the
flywheel to the three floors of the works by a
rope race running up the end of the building.
The building itself was purposely constructed
as a rope works and the chimney carries the
Diamond Ropeworks emblem.

When rope making ceased engine and boiler
were redundant, but the new owners, Sammy-
Woodland Ltd, were anxious that they should
be preserved. They are now in the care of the
Northern Mill Engines Society. Access is on
open days arranged by the owners and the
Society. Details are obtainable from the Secretary, NMES, 248 Northwich Road, Weaver-
ham, Cheshire.

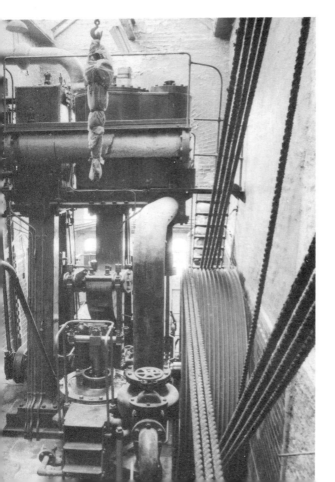

*Diamond Works. A typical Scott
& Hodgson design of inverted
vertical compound engine. The air
pump is driven by a rocking arm
from the LP crosshead. Note also
the rope 'race' taking the drive to
several floors.*

DOGDYKE PUMPING STATION,
Tattershall, Lincs

A-FRAME SINGLE BEAM ENGINE & SCOOP
WHEEL
(Probably) Bradley & Craven, Wakefield,
1855, 24 in × 42 in, slide valve, Watt-type
governor, single plate cast-iron beam 12 ft 3 in
centres, cruciform connecting rod, flywheel
16 ft diameter, 28 rpm, scoop wheel 28 ft diameter, 7 rpm.

A very interesting installation, built right at the
end of the beam engine and scoop wheel era for
fen drainage. Later scoop wheels were driven
by other forms of engine and, more importantly
by the general introduction of the centrifugal
pump was just around the corner. This engine
served until 1940 when a Ruston diesel engine
and Gwynnes pump was installed. From 1909
steam was provided by a 6 ft × 16 ft Lancashire
boiler by William Foster. Preservation was
initiated by Messrs Burton and Porter in 1969
and a trust was later formed. The engine has
been restored to working order and a vertical
boiler put in to supply steam.

Access is on open days and summer Sundays
and details should be obtained from J. G.
Porter, Bridge Farm, Tattershall, Lincoln,
LN4 4JG

ENGLEFIELD ESTATE SAWMILL, Berkshire

SINGLE CYLINDER HORIZONTAL MILL
ENGINES (2)
Ransomes Sims & Jefferies, Ipswich, No
12885, 1889, 12 in × 24 in, expansion slide
valves, link motion valve-gear, Hartnell type
high-speed governor, girder bed, trunk crosshead guides, disc crank.
Clayton & Shuttleworth, Lincoln, 1863, 7 in ×
14 in, slide valve, Watt type governor, 'bent'
forged crankshaft.
Cornish boiler 5 ft 6 in × 20 ft, H. & T. Danks,
Netherton, 1899, 100 psi.

The Boiler and Ransomes engine were installed by John Wilder, Engineers of Reading. It is
a fine example of the ultimate development of
the single-cylinder slide-valve engine. Ransomes used a link motion similar to Stephenson's to drive the expansion valve which was
controlled by the governor to alter the cut-off,
giving maximum economy. At Englefield full
economy was not realised, as having plenty of
sawdust and off cuts for fuel simplicity pre-
vailed and the exhaust goes straight to atmosphere. Drive to the mill was by flat belt
from a pulley alongside the flywheel. Boiler
feed is supplied by a diagonal single ram-pump
driven by an eccentric on the crankshaft.

The Clayton engine is an example of the
earlier designs of horizontal engine with flat
table-like bed and four-bar crosshead guides.
The governor operates a throttle valve. The
starting valve with neat handle is as old as the
engine and has a socket 'rust' joint connection
to the steam pipe. Exhaust is to atmosphere.
Drive to the mill was by flat belt from a pulley
alongside the flywheel.

The sawmill still operates with electric
drives, but the engines are in the care of
members of the Thames Valley Traction Engine Club. Details of access which is normally
on steam open days, should be obtained from
the club. (The Club chairman is R.
Hawthorne, 19, Bridle Path, Woodcote,
Reading.)

*Englefield Sawmill. Ransomes, Sims & Jefferies
of 1899 with all the Eastern England hall-marks.
Girder bed, trunk cross-head guides, disc crank
and a link motion expansion valve gear are all
here. The high-speed spring loaded governor was
sensitive and well suited to cut-off control.*

D. GURTEEN & SONS LTD,
Chauntry Mill, Haverhill, Suffolk

SINGLE CYLINDER HORIZONTAL MILL
ENGINE
Hick, Hargreaves & Co, Bolton, 1879, 18 in ×
48 in, Corliss valves, Inglis & Spencer trip
gear, girder bed, trunk crosshead guides, flywheel 17 ft diameter grooved for four ropes,
120 hp, 60 rpm, 80 psi, non-condensing.

A superb example of an older generation of
mill engine using steam at fairly low pressure
in a single cylinder with economy derived from
the use of Corliss valves. In the northern textile
industry many engines of this type were later
compounded by the addition of a tandem high
pressure cylinder taking steam at up to 160 psi.
This engine however has remained in its
original form. The flywheel which has the
spokes boarded in, is behind the engine house
wall and a walkway allows the flywheel and
rope-race to be examined. The engine is named
Caroline after Mrs Caroline Gurteen and was
started on 3 January 1880.

Access is on open days when the engine is
run under steam, and at other times by
application.

*Chauntry Mill. An impressive flywheel with some
equally impressive carpentry work on the
boarding.*

*Chauntry Mill. Hick, Hargreaves of Bolton were
early exponents of the girder bed design as seen
here on Caroline of 1879.*

MILLMEECE PUMPING STATION,
Eccleshall, Staffs

HORIZONTAL TANDEM COMPOUND
WATERWORKS PUMPING ENGINES (2)
Ashton, Frost, Blackburn, 1914, 27in (HP),
39in (LP) × 60in stroke, Corliss valves, governor controlled trip-gear HP, hand adjusted
trip gear LP, tail-rod drive to double-acting
force pump, trunk crosshead guides, surface
condenser.
Hathorn, Davey, Leeds, 1926, 29in (HP), 42in
(LP) × 60in stroke, Corliss valves (details as
above), tail-rod drive to force pump and
outdoor angle-bobs over well. Three Lancashire boilers, 160psi, Green's economiser,
superheaters, Hodgkinson-Bennis underfeed
stokers, Green's single-cylinder horizontal
engine driving economiser scraper-gear.

Two engines built to the same specification
which illustrate the difference in detail resulting from each manufacturer's interpretation of
customer requirements. The Ashton, Frost
engine has a two bearing crankshaft and an
overhung single-web crank. The Hathorn,
Davey engine is altogether more massive with
larger cylinders, a three-bearing crankshaft
and double-web crank. As built the Ashton,

Frost engine also drove a set of outdoor well
pumps through angle bobs, but during its
career the bed fractured and the well pumps
were removed to lighten the load. Pumping
from the well to the well head was thereafter
performed by vertical-shaft electric centrifugal
pumps when this engine was in use.

The Millmeece plant was not taken out of
commission until 1980 and was the last in
service with tandem compound engines. The
station remains in full service with electric
pumps. Access is on open days or by prior
arrangement with the Divisional Manager,
Severn-Trent Water Authority, Upper Trent
Division, Westport Road, Burslem, Stoke-on-
Trent, ST6 4JT.

*Millmeece. Ashton, Frost tandem compound
pumping engine of 1914. The force pump driven
by the LP tail rod is behind the camera. Also
driven by the tail rod by a rocking arm is the
underfloor condenser air pump.*

Millmeece. The Hathorn Davey engine had precisely the same layout as the earlier Ashton, Frost engine, but the engine itself was larger with more massive proportions.

WESTONZOYLAND PUMPING STATION, Bridgwater, Somerset

TWIN CYLINDER VERTICAL A-FRAME DRAINAGE PUMPING ENGINE
Easton, Amos & Sons, London, 1861, 20 in × 24 in, Meyer expansion slide-valves, (fixed cut-off), parallel-motion crosshead-guides, jet condenser, bevel-gear drive to Appold vertical-spindle centrifugal pump, 50 rpm, 60 psi. Lancashire boiler, E. Danks, Oldbury, 1914, No 1048, 75 psi.

The Westonzoyland engine is virtually identical to the Curry Moor engine. The engine house was built in 1830-1 for a 27 hp beam engine and scoop wheel; these were replaced in 1861 by the present engine, which worked until 1951. A Robey locomotive-type portable boiler is being restored to provide steam.

Also on display are engines and boilers from various locations:

SINGLE CYLINDER HORIZONTAL ENGINE
W. & F. Wills, Bridgwater, 1886, 9 in × 15 in. Flywheel 7 ft 0 in diameter.

This engine was used at a local brick and tile works. It incorporates Wills's patent valve gear, consisting of two double-beat valves for inlet, and two for exhaust, lifted open by variable cams sliding on a shaft which is driven by a bevel gear on the crankshaft. A spring governor regulates cut-off by varying the position of the cams on the shaft.

INVERTED VERTICAL ENGINE
Maker unknown, approx 1885, 5 in × 8 in, flywheel 3 ft 1 in diameter. The frame and cylinder are cast in one piece.

There are a number of feed pumps from a brewery in Wiveliscombe, Somerset, as well as two vertical boilers.

The pumping station is open most Sunday afternoons in the summer, and the first Sunday of the month in winter, when restoration work is in progress. Open days are held at Easter, Spring and August Bank Holidays.

Access   by   Arrangement Only

ABERGORKI COLLIERY,
Mountain Ash, Glamorgan

> WADDLE MINE VENTILATING FAN &
> DUPLICATE FAN ENGINE
> Waddle Patent Fan & Engineering Co Ltd,
> Llanelli, c1880, 20 in × 36 in, slide valves,
> 80 psi.

The 'Waddle' fan is of the centrifugal type, ie
the air enters the fan at the centre or 'eye' and is
flung out radially along the blades to escape at
the periphery. Generally a centrifugal fan
requires a housing with a specially shaped
outlet or evasee, but the Waddle fan, apart
from an inlet duct to direct the air the eye,
requires no housing and it rotates in the open.
The air exhausted from the mine merely
escapes around the rim of the fan. It was
normal practice to couple the Waddle fan
directly to the crankshaft of the engine, which
as in this case was usually horizontal. As the fan
runner was of considerable weight this acted as
a flywheel and a separate one was not necessary.

The Abergorki fan was scheduled as an
ancient monument in 1969, but is not yet
restored and interior viewing is not normally
possible.

ALLER MOOR PUMPING STATION,
Burrowbridge, Somerset

> TWIN CYLINDER A-FRAME VERTICAL
> ENGINE & CENTRIFUGAL PUMP
> Easton Amos & Anderson, London, 1869,
> 13½ in × 24 in, Meyer expansion slide-valves,
> disc cranks, non-condensing, geared to
> vertical-spindle centrifugal pump, 50 rpm.
> Dished-end Lancashire boiler, John Thomp-
> son, Wolverhampton, 1924, 60 psi.

Large scale land drainage is usually associated
with the fens of the eastern counties, but
similar problems were found in the sedge
moors of Somerset. The Aller Moor installation is quite an early example of the use of a
high-speed centrifugal pump geared up from a

slow-speed steam engine. The pump is located
at the bottom of a deep sump with a vertical
shaft driven from the engine crankshaft
through bevel gears. For quietness of operation the large gear has hardwood teeth. This
pumping system was also used in the fen
district, but the only survivors are in Somerset.

Aller Moor engine is very plain indeed and
the Meyer expansion valves have fixed cut-off.
Feed water was supplied by a diagonal engine-
driven ram pump. A twin-cylinder diagonal
engine and a twin-cylinder inverted-vertical
engine from other locations are now exhibited
at Aller Moor.

Access is by arrangement with Mr L. W.
Musgrave, Aller Moor Cottage, Burrowbridge, Bridgwater, Somerset, Phone: Burrowbridge 324.

*Aller Moor. A later engine than Curry Moor but
from the same manufacturer. There are several
noticeable differences in construction. Note the
marine-type big-end.*

APPLETON PUMPING STATION,
Sandringham Estate, Norfolk

Pratchitt Bros, Carlisle, 1877, 9 in × 18 in, Meyer expansion slide valve, disc crank, flywheel 7 ft diameter, gear drive to three-throw vertical ram pump. Cornish boiler.

This small installation pumped to an ornamental water tower which supplied a considerable area. The tower, which also serves as a dwelling, is a considerable landmark in the district. Although a small and simple plant regard was paid to economy in working. The cylinder is steam jacketted and exhaust is to a jet condenser behind the cylinder, the air pump being driven by the tail rod.

The plant has been cleaned and painted and is partially restored. Access is by application to the Estate Office.

Appleton. Even in a small waterworks attention was given to economy in working and neatness of design. This is witnessed by the condenser, expansion slide valves and polished wood lagged cylinder secured by brass bands.

BAITING MILL, Norden, Rochdale, Lancs

HORIZONTAL TANDEM COMPOUND MILL ENGINE
S. S. Stott & Co Ltd, Haslingdon, 1895, 12 in (HP), 24 in (LP) × 36 in stroke (approx), Corliss valves HP, slide valve LP, Lumb's governor, 250 hp, 140 psi, named *Mary*. One Lancashire boiler 7 ft × 28 ft, Hill's of Heywood 1913, economiser by Goodbrand of Stalybridge.

Baiting Mill. S. S. Stott built a neat but very robust design of engine. Here the slide valve LP cylinder has wood lagging, while the Corliss HP cylinder has blued steel cladding.

The mill and power plant are typical of the once numerous and familiar Lancashire village weaving 'shed'. The boiler, now oil fired, is still in use and the Goodbrand economiser, similar to the almost universal Green's, adds what is now an unfamiliar item. Drive from the engine crankshaft was taken directly through the engine house wall, although latterly the mill lineshafting was disconnected and an alternator was driven through pulleys.

For access application should be made to Cudworth Bros (Norden) Ltd, at the mill.

Baiting Mill. It was common practice to name engines in the textile mills of Lancashire and Yorkshire. Even moderately powered engines such as this S. S. Scott tandem compound were started with due ceremony by the mill owner's wife or daughter.

BEELEIGH MILL, Green Bros, Malden, Essex

WOOLF COMPOUND BEAM MILL ENGINE
Wentworth & Son, Wandsworth, 1845, 12 in × 30 in (HP), 15 in × 40 in (LP) approx.

Compared with the number of existing Woolf-compound pumping engines, surviving mill engines of this type are few. It will be noted from the date that Wentworth's were using the compound system as soon as available steam pressures made this viable.

Access is by prior application to the mill.

BESTWOOD COLLIERY, Nottingham

TWIN CYLINDER VERTICAL WINDING ENGINE
R. J. & E. Coupe, Worsley Mesnes Ironworks, Wigan, 1873, 36 in × 72 in, 80 psi.

This is the last survivor of a once very popular type of winding engine. As a natural development of the single cylinder 'Durham' type the design was capable of fast winding in deep shafts. Its use was widespread and it was made by a variety of builders and to large sizes. The Bestwood engine is believed to have come second-hand from South Wales. It is in the care of Nottinghamshire County Council but as yet is unrestored and not accessible for viewing.

BLAGDON PUMPING STATION,
Bristol Waterworks Co

WOOLF COMPOUND WATERWORKS PUMPING
ENGINES (2)
Glenfield & Kennedy, Kilmarnock, 1902, 21 in
× 62 in (HP), 34 in × 84 in (LP), Cornish valves,
Porter governor, twin-plate cast-iron beam,
17 rpm, 200 hp, 100 psi, raw water from reservoir to treatment works, 250 ft head.

Two late engines built in traditional style with considerable ornamentation. The use of cast-iron for the beams at such a late date is noteworthy, as Glenfield's favoured cast-iron. The engines are house-built with fluted cast-iron columns under the beam trunnions. Cylinders have polished wood-strip lagging secured by brass bands. Valve gear is cam operated through an underfloor layshaft with bevel gear drive from the crankshaft. Levers in a quadrant frame are provided for hand working the valves at starting. The high-pressure inlet valves have hand adjusted trip gear to vary the cut-off. A single force-pump is driven from the outdoor end of the beam by rods without parallel motion. One concession to modernity is the barring engine, inverted vertical, which engages an internal toothed ring on the flywheel rim.

Access is by application (usually parties only) to the Engineer & Manager, Bristol Waterworks Co, Bedminster Down, Bristol.

Blagdon. Trip gear with adjusting handwheel. Beyond on the long spindle is the handwheel controlling the throttle valve.

Blagdon. The beam chamber. Even on these late engines the beams are cast iron.

BRAYTON PUMPING STATION, Selby, Yorks

INVERTED VERTICAL TRIPLE EXPANSION WATERWORKS PUMPING ENGINE
James Watt & Co, 1906, 13 in (HP), 20 in (IP), 34 in (LP) × 24 in stroke, 27 rpm, 150 psi, 90 hp (approx).

This is quite a small engine and it is interesting to compare it with the Roall installation not far away. The Brayton engine represents contemporary technology, while the Roall engine was rapidly becoming an old-fashioned type when installed. A small Davey, Paxman inverted-vertical compound engine is also preserved in the workshops.

Access is by application to the Yorkshire Water Authority, South Eastern Division, Copley House, Waterdale, Doncaster, South Yorks.

BREDE PUMPING STATION,
St Leonard's, Sussex

INVERTED VERTICAL TRIPLE EXPANSION WATERWORKS PUMPING ENGINE
Tangye & Co, Birmingham, 1904, Meyer expansion slide valves HP and IP, simple slide valve LP, surface condenser.

Triple expansion inverted engines with slide valves are now extremely rare, and this one with its long eccentric rods is particularly elegant. Originally the engine drove well pumps and force pumps but the well pump mechanism was disconnected in 1933, the drive then being taken from an electric motor by the English Electric Co. The engine is beautifully preserved and it is likely that it will eventually be transferred to the Brighton & Hove Engineerium.

Access is by application to the Southern Water Authority, East Sussex Division, Menzies Rd, St Leonard's-on-Sea, Sussex.

BRERETON MILL, Holmes Chapel, Cheshire

SINGLE CYLINDER HORIZONTAL MILL ENGINE
Edwin Foden, Sandbach, possibly 1860s, 12 in × 32 in, slide valve, Porter governor, jet condenser, gear drive to mill. Cornish boiler, E. Foden & Sons, Sandbach.

At Brereton the engine was installed to assist a waterwheel which still exists, and the engine drove by gearing onto the second, or mill, shaft. Reputedly the engine ceased work in 1914. The inscription on the boiler firedoor is E. Foden & Sons indicating that either the boiler itself or the firedoor is a replacement. As preserved the engine is not as yet restored and the mill itself is a private residence. Prior application should be made for access to the engine.

BRINDLEY BANK PUMPING STATION,
Rugeley, Staffs

HORIZONTAL TANDEM COMPOUND PUMPING ENGINE
Hathorn, Davey & Co Ltd, Leeds, 1907, 36 in (HP), 72 in (LP) × 72 in stroke, Meyer expansion slide valves, double-web crank, angle bobs and spears to well pumps driven from main crankpin, tail-rod drive to double-acting force pump, surface condenser, 20 rpm, 100 psi.

A large engine to be fitted with slide valves, but under the control of a first-class station engineer the efficiency was as high as could be obtained. The silence of operation was remarkable. Inevitably this layout of engine and

Brindley Bank. The Hathorn, Davey tandem compound was a large engine to be fitted with slide valves, but the quietness of operation was exceptional. The engine drew water from a well by two angle-bob driven pumps driven from the crankpin and delivered into the mains by a force pump coupled to the LP tail rod.

pumps gives a long installation and it is interesting to compare it with Fleam Dyke by the same maker where all drives are from the tail rod and the whole of the pumping plant is behind the engine. There is a collection of waterworks equipment in the former boiler-house.

Access is by application to the South Staffordshire Waterworks Company, Engineer's Office, Sheepcote Lane, Birmingham, B16 8AR.

BRITISH LEYLAND, Chorley, Lancs

HORIZONTAL CROSS COMPOUND MILL
ENGINE
Clayton, Goodfellow & Co Ltd, Blackburn, 1914, Nos 566 & 567, cylinders approx 16 in (HP), 32 in (LP) × 42 in stroke, Corliss valves, Craig's cut-off, Whitehead governor, jet condenser behind LP cylinder, flywheel 16 ft 6 in diameter, grooved for ten ropes (eight ropes on), approx 600 hp, rope drive to 400 kW DC generator by Lancashire Dynamo & Motor Company.

The works was built in 1914 as a cotton weaving mill, but due to World War I was never opened as such and after the war were purchased by the then Leyland Motors. The installation is highly interesting as it represents an intermediate phase in textile mill drives

between engine-driven lineshafts and individual motor drives with power purchased from public supply. The 'shed' here was laid out with lineshafts to drive traditional Lancashire looms and although the disposition of drives is not known now, it is possible that one motor was arranged to drive a pair of lineshafts. Individual motor drives for looms followed soon after this installation and in 1916 Messrs Simpson & Godlee of Swinton built a new weaving shed with all looms individually driven and power taken from the public supply.

At Chorley the engine is a classic Clayton, Goodfellow design with Craig's cut-off gear governor controlled on the HP cylinder and hand adjusted on the LP. The engine layout keeps practically all parts above the floor and the only significant item below floor level is the boiler feed-pump. This is driven by an eccentric from the crankshaft and a downward inclined rod.

Access is by prior arrangement and permit from British Leyland, Leyland Parts Ltd, Grime Street, Chorley, Lancs.

British Leyland. The flywheel of this Clayton, Goodfellow engine is made up of two halves and is secured to the crankshaft by four stakes. This view is from the LP side of the engine. Note the very plain engine house with concrete floor and a minimum of wall tiling.

BROKEN SCAR WATERWORKS, TEES COTTAGE WORKS, Darlington, Co Durham

WOOLF COMPOUND WATERWORKS PUMPING ENGINE
Teasdale Bros,Darlington, 1904, 18 in × 63 in (HP), 29 in × 84 in (LP),Cornish valves, hand-adjusted trip gear, Porter governor, twin-plate cast-iron beam 28 ft between centres by 5 ft deep, flywheel 21 ft diameter, river pump (lift type) 25½ in × 72 in, 1,900 gpm, 30 ft head, town pump (bucket & ram type) 32 in × 42 in, internal ram 23 in diameter, 1,800 gpm, 125 ft head, 140 hp, 16 rpm. Two Lancashire boilers 7 ft 6 in × 28 ft, Teasdale Bros, forced draught furnaces, 100 psi, single cylinder 'Cameron' feed pump, and an injector.

Tees Cottage works commenced operations in 1849, having been built by The Darlington Gas & Water Co to extract water from the River Tees and supply the town of Darlington. Two beam engines were installed in separate houses with boiler plants at each. All these original buildings survive. The present beam engine was erected in a new house.

Broken Scar. The beam chamber viewed from the ▲ cylinder end of the beam.

The river pump drew water from the Tees and delivered to sand filters. The town pump delivered filtered water into the town supply mains. Both pumps are coupled by rods to the crankshaft end of the beam. Below the driving floor is the condenser air pump and the 'jack-head' or condenser cooling water pump and these are coupled by rods to the cylinder end of the beam. An underfloor layshaft, bevel geared to the crankshaft, drives a cam and roller system operating the valve gear. Hand levers were fitted to work the valves when starting the engine. Although this is a late example of a beam engine, the whole of the cast-iron work is highly decorated, giving the impression of a much older engine.

Of the other 1849 beam engine, its buildings were adapted in 1913 to house a twin-cylinder horizontal Hornsby-Stockport gas engine developing 220 hp at 200 rpm, but normally working at 125 rpm and giving a similar output to the 1904 beam engine at this speed. This engine drove two sets of three-throw vertical ram-pumps made by Hathorn Davey. All survive including a small single cylinder gas engine for charging the air receiver for starting. Also surviving is the suction gas plant, where gas was made from anthracite to supply the gas engine.

Broken Scar. The packing floor showing decorated valve chest, cylinder tops, with 'suet' lubricators, pipes for cover jacket steam and indicator cocks.

Access to the works is by application to the Northumbrian Water Authority, Tees Division.

113

BROMSBERROW PUMPING STATION, Glos

HORIZONTAL SIDE-BY-SIDE COMPOUND
PUMPING ENGINE
Tangyes Ltd, Birmingham, 1928.

Although new when installed for Malvern Urban District Council, steam power for the small waterworks was almost at an end. Nevertheless the side-by-side compound made a compact and economical unit and this example served for some 42 years.

Access is by application to the Severn-Trent Water Authority, Lower Severn Division, Southwick Park, Gloucester Road, Tewksbury, Glos.

Bromsberrow Pumping Station. Tangye's adapted what was a mill engine design to water pumping. A borehole pump was gear driven from the flywheel end of the crankshaft and a set of force pumps (now removed) from the coupling flange seen on the right of this picture. Meyer expansion slide valves are fitted to HP and LP cylinders. ▼

CHELVEY PUMPING STATION,
Bristol Waterworks Co

INVERTED VERTICAL TRIPLE EXPANSION
WATERWORKS PUMPING ENGINE
The Lilleshall Company, Oakengates, 1923, 20 in (HP), 35 in (IP), 56 in (LP) × 42 in stroke, drop valves, superheated steam 160 psi, 260 hp, 24 rpm, 4 mgd, two well pumps, three force pumps.

The last conventional steam engine supplied to the Bristol Waterworks Co, it is one of two Lilleshall triple-expansion waterworks engines in preservation. The lift pumps in the well were driven directly by a two-throw extension of the engine crankshaft beyond the flywheel. The force pumps below the engine bed were driven by side rods from the crossheads.

Access is usually available to organised parties only by application to the Company at Bedminster Down, Bristol.

Upper Cherry Garden. Triple expansion tandem cylinders of duplex pump. The LP is centre with IP in front and HP behind. With all those unlagged transfer pipes one wonders at the water content of the steam in the LP cylinders. ▶

CHERRY GARDEN PUMPING STATION, Folkestone, Kent

TRIPLE EXPANSION DUPLEX PUMPING ENGINES (2)
James Simpson & Co, Pimlico, 1889, Nos 2379 & 2380. 7 in (HP), 10 in (IP), 17½ in (LP) × 15 in stroke, slide valves, surface condenser, 80 psi.

The 'Duplex' pump was the invention of Henry Worthington of New York and was built under licence in Britain by James Simpson. Ultimately the two firms were combined as Worthington-Simpson, who still manufacture pumps at Newark-on-Trent. The Worthington duplex pump was direct-acting without a flywheel, the pumps being directly coupled to the piston rods. Two steam cylinders were fixed side-by-side and the valve gear of one was operated by linkage from the piston rod of the other. Each side of the engine was thus made to work alternately. Duplex pumps were made simple, compound and triple-expansion, the cylinders being arranged in tandem on the multiple expansion engines.

At upper Cherry Garden the high-pressure cylinders are at the rear, low pressure in the middle and intermediate at the front. The cylinders are adjacent with common covers and internal neck glands for the piston rod to pass through. Transfer pipes between the cylinders are copper and unlagged. One wonders at the water content of the steam in the low-pressure cylinder. The cylinders themselves are lagged with wood strips secured by brass bands. Exhaust is to a surface condenser mounted above the pumps, and when the engines were in service cooling was by water en route to the town mains. The air pump is driven by an extension of one of the pump rods. Beneath the engine house floor is a reservoir from which the engines pumped. The water level is indicated by a float to which was attached a vertical rod passing upwards through a hole in the floor.

The workshops were driven by a small steeple engine (also preserved) with cylinder about 6 in × 12 in. This interesting little engine was non-condensing, the exhaust being used for space heating in winter. One of the duplex pumps can be run under steam supplied by a Robey locomotive-type portable boiler. This in itself is a worthy item, being about 105 years old and still in almost perfect condition.

Upper Cherry Garden. The side-by-side compound made a compact design of waterworks pump. In this Robey built engine attention has been paid to economy combined with simplicity, as evidenced by the re-heater between HP and LP stages. The engine is seen here in its working location at Denge Marsh.

A number of other pumping engines, mostly small, have been brought to Upper Cherry Garden from other locations. These include the following.

> HORIZONTAL SIDE-BY-SIDE COMPOUND PUMPING ENGINE
> FROM DENGE MARSH WATERWORKS
> Robey & Co Ltd, Lincoln, 1918, for Worthington-Simpson, 8¼ in (HP), 13 in (LP) × 12 in stroke, Meyer expansion slide valves hand adjusted on HP, fixed cut-off on LP, balanced cranks, diagonal boiler feed-pump, surface condenser, tail-rod drive to Duplex double-acting force pumps.

Built by Robey & Co under sub-contract to Worthington-Simpson the engine is a smaller example of the side-by-side layout and well illustrates the compactness of this design. Although quite a small engine, the cylinders are separate castings and not made in one block, as was done by other Eastern England builders.

> TWIN CYLINDER HORIZONTAL ENGINE
> FROM SHEARWAY PUMPING STATION
> Maker unknown c1860, 3 in × 6 in approx, slide valves.

Although little more than a model, this engine was once used to drive a small generator for electric lighting. The slide valves are on top of the cylinders, worked by rocker arms.

> INVERTED VERTICAL TWIN CYLINDER DONKEY PUMP
> FROM LOWER STANDEN WATERWORKS
> Frank Pearn & Co Ltd, Manchester, c1910, 5 in × 5 in stroke.

Access to Upper Cherry Garden, which is still an operational waterworks using electric pumps, is by application to the Folkestone & District Water Co, Cherry Garden Lane, Folkestone, Kent, CT10 4QB.

C. & J. CLARK,
Shoe Manufacturers, Street, Somerset

> HORIZONTAL TANDEM COMPOUND MILL
> ENGINE
> Cole, Marchent & Morley, Bradford, 1909,
> named *Anthony*, 12 in (HP), 24 in (LP) × 36 in
> stroke, piston drop-valves, girder bed, trunk
> crosshead-guides, flywheel 12 ft diameter
> grooved for wire ropes, jet condenser behind
> LP cylinder, 250 hp, 140 psi, 100 rpm

Cole Marchent & Morley played a great part in the development of the piston drop-valve. Having little inertia and suitable for highly superheated steam the piston drop-valve meant that engines could run with high economy at higher revolutions than other types. In 1906 the firm took the record for the most economical engine installed up to that date, returning a steam consumption of 8·58 pounds per ihp, per hour. C. & J. Clark's engine was started on 1 January 1910 and gave 40 years service. The firm thought this was worthy of an honourable retirement and the engine is kept in full working order and in immaculate condition. The engine can be run for demonstration purposes by connection to the factory compressed air system.

Also preserved, this time in the works power house, is a Belliss & Morcom inverted-vertical compound high-speed enclosed engine of about 1913. Having two piston valves on parallel axes it represents the transition period between the earlier engines with a single multi-ported piston valve and the two piston-valve type with valves in vee formation.

Access is by prior application to the firm's Public Relations Manager.

C. & J. Clark. The piston drop valves are operated by eccentrics on a layshaft, bevel gear driven from the crankshaft. Note the quadrant which adjusts the LP cut-off. The engine could be operated with extraction between HP and LP cylinders and a servo-valve system determined the LP cut-off in accordance with extraction steam demand.

Clay Mills. Beam and parallel motion linkage of Woolf compound engine 'B'. Note the wrought iron box girder construction of the beam.

CLAY MILLS SEWAGE WORKS, Burton-on-Trent, Staffs

WOOLF COMPOUND SEWAGE PUMPING ENGINES (4)
Gimson & Co, Leicester, 1885, 24in × 6ft (HP), 38in × 8ft (LP), Cornish double-beat valves, wrought-iron box section beam 28ft long, flywheel 24ft diameter 6-12rpm, 80psi, two sewage pumps 21in × 6ft stroke. Five Lancashire boilers.

These are excellent examples of large Woolf-compound house-built engines, contained in two engine houses with the boiler house between. The valves are operated by under-floor cam gear driven by bevel gearing from the crankshaft. Cylindrical weights, known as 'top hats' at Clay Mills, ensured closure of the valves when released by the cams. Exhaust steam passed to an underfloor jet condenser, the air pump alongside being operated by a vertical rod connected by parallel motion to the beam. The sewage pumps are below the engine in a deep basement, and are located each side of the beam fulcrum. The 'outdoor' pump is coupled to the beam by rods, but the 'indoor' pump is coupled to the HP piston tail rod.

The present five boilers replaced the originals in 1937 and are fitted with a twin set of Green's economisers, and Meldrum's mechanical stokers. The boilers also supplied steam to over thirty auxiliary engines which performed a host of pumping and driving duties.

Access is by application to the Engineer at the Works, which is operated by the Severn-Trent Water Authority.

Clay Mills. Top nozzles of engine 'B', with 'top hats'.

Clay Mills. Driving floor view. Bottom nozzles on left and 'top hats' on the valve spindles. Note the expansion pieces in the pipes connecting top and bottom nozzles.

COTTINGHAM PUMPING STATION, Hull, Yorks

INVERTED VERTICAL TRIPLE EXPANSION WATERWORKS PUMPING ENGINE
Worthington-Simpson Ltd, Newark-on-Trent, 1930.

This engine is one of three installed here in 1930. Well pumps were driven by an extension of the engine crankshaft, with force pumps below the engine bed having side rod drive from the crossheads.

Access is by application to the Yorkshire Water Authority, Eastern Division, Essex House, Manor St, Kingston-upon-Hull.

CROSS LANE MILL, Peter Green & Sons, Low Bradley, Skipton, Yorks

TANDEM COMPOUND MILL ENGINE
Smith Bros & Eastwood, Bradford, 1901, 14 in (HP), 28 in (LP) × 42 in stroke. Corliss valves, Lumb's governor, 14 ft 6 in flywheel grooved for eight ropes, 80 rpm, 300 hp, named *Progress*. Lancashire boiler 8 ft × 30 ft, 135 psi. Proctor's shovel type mechanical stokers, Green's 64-tube economiser.

Smith Bros & Eastwood appear to have been more millwrights than engine makers, and so far as is known they only built three engines. They must have built well for *Progress* drove Cross Lane Mill for 77 years. The boiler also supplied steam at full working pressure throughout the engine's working life. Engine and boiler were installed to replace a beam engine and this is quite apparent from the configuration of the engine house. Speed control is by cut-off on the HP inlet valves, with hand adjustment on the LP. The LP cylinder is behind the HP and the jet condenser in turn is behind the LP cylinder. The air pump is driven by an extension of the LP piston tail rod. A diagonal ram-type boiler feed-pump is driven by an eccentric from the outer end of the crankshaft on the other side of the engine house wall. A small oil-fired boiler has been installed for heating with a connection to the engine so that it can be run light.

Access for viewing the engine is by prior application to the mill.

Cross Lane Mill. This Smith Bros & Eastwood engine with Corliss valves on HP and LP cylinders was named Progress.

CROSSNESS SEWAGE WORKS, London

TRIPLE EXPANSION BEAM PUMPING ENGINES (4)
James Watt & Co, Soho Works, Birmingham, 1865, rebuilt by Benjamin Goodfellow, Hyde, 1899, 19 in × 7 ft 10½ in (HP), 32 in × 7 ft 10½ in (IP), 44 in × 9 ft (LP).

Crossness on the South Bank, and Abbey Mills on the North Bank of the River Thames were built as part of the London trunk sewer schemes of the 1850s and 60s, and were designed to eliminate the multiplicity of sewage discharges into the river in Central London. At both stations the pumping engines were housed in vast ornate engine houses with much decorative cast-iron work. Only at Crossness do the engines survive, and these are arranged in a cruciform layout. As built the engines were single cylinder taking steam at about 30 psi. To achieve greater economy and higher power in conjunction with higher steam pressure, the rebuilding to triple expansion was undertaken. This rebuilding is one of the now rare examples of Goodfellow's work.

The engines are preserved but not restored and access is by permit only from the Thames Water Authority, Metropolitan Public Health Division, 50-64 Broadway, Westminster, London, SW1.

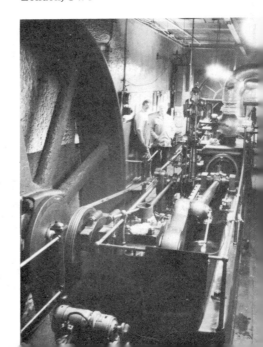

120

CURRY MOOR PUMPING STATION, Burrowbridge, Somerset

> TWIN CYLINDER A-FRAME VERTICAL
> ENGINE & CENTRIFUGAL PUMP
> Easton, Amos & Sons, London, 1864, 20 in ×
> 24 in, Meyer fixed cut-off expansion slide
> valves, jet condenser, parallel motion to piston
> rods, 50 rpm, geared to vertical-spindle cent-
> rifugal pump.

An earlier engine than at Aller Moor, this condenses the exhaust steam. Its antiquity is emphasised by the parallel-motion guiding the piston rods. The parallel-motion linkage is also used to drive the condenser air pump and the boiler feed-pump. Apart from these details the layout of the engine and pump is similar to Aller Moor. The pumping station was re-modelled in the 1950s and two Ruston diesel engines installed. The engine can be turned by an electric motor.

Access arrangements are as for Aller Moor Pumping Station (p 107).

Curry Moor. Twin cylinder vertical engine coupled to a centrifugal pump. The piston rod is guided by parallel motion and the large bevel gear wheel has hardwood teeth.

Curry Moor. The parallel motion also transmits the drive to the condenser air pump and boiler feed pump.

DALMORE DISTILLERY,
Alnes, Ross & Cromarty

SINGLE CYLINDER HORIZONTAL ENGINE
SINGLE CYLINDER INVERTED ENGINE
James Milne & Co, Edinburgh, c1885 (inverted vertical), and same maker 1898 (horizontal).

Two small engines which formerly drove machinery at the distillery and are now preserved. James Milne & Co were not primarily engine builders, but made engines so that a complete plant could be supplied. This applied to many engineering concerns in the nineteenth century.

Access is by application to Mackenzie Bros (Dalmore) Ltd, at the distillery.

DEVENISH WEYMOUTH BREWERY,
Weymouth, Dorset

SINGLE CYLINDER HORIZONTAL ENGINE
Barrett, Exhall & Andrews, Reading, date unknown, 11 in × 15 in approx.

A small engine and the last known survivor of this make. Access is by application to the brewery.

DENGE PUMPING STATION, Folkestone, Kent

SIDE-BY-SIDE COMPOUND WATERWORKS PUMPING ENGINE
Supplied by Worthington.Simpson Ltd, built by Robey & Co, Lincoln, 1934, No 47803, 14 in (HP), 19½ in (LP) × 20 in stroke, Meyer expansion slide-valves, hand adjusted on HP, fixed cut-off on LP, Pickering governor, surface condenser, tail-rod drive to duplex double-acting force pump and condenser air-pump, diagonal boiler feed-pump eccentric driven from crankshaft, 125 psi.

The side-by-side compound layout was a favourite with Eastern England builders for the smaller powers and was closely related to the portable and semi-portable engines of the same manufacture. This engine has independent cylinders, but in the smaller examples the high and low pressure cylinders were usually cast in one block. This engine is now partly dismantled.

Access is by application to the Folkestone & District Water Co, Cherry Garden Lane, Folkestone, Kent, CT19 4QB.

Denge Marsh. Side-by-side compound made by Robey for Worthington-Simpson. The tail rods drive a double-acting duplex force pump. The cylinders are overhung from the bedplate.

DOVER PUMPING STATION, Kent

INVERTED VERTICAL TRIPLE EXPANSION WATERWORKS PUMPING ENGINE
Worthington-Simpson Ltd, Newark-on-Trent, 1937, No 5055, 14 in (HP), 24 in (IP), 36 in (LP) × 36 in stroke, piston drop-valves, 22 rpm, 185 psi superheated, 147 hp, three-throw well pumps, three force pumps below engine bed.

Commissioned in 1939 this engine replaced a Woolf-compound beam engine in the same house and was itself replaced by electric pumps in 1977. The well pumps were driven by a three-throw extension of the engine crankshaft beyond the flywheel and these pumps delivered into an impressive service reservoir with vaulted roof constructed in the 1850s. The three force-pumps driven by side rods from the engine cross-heads delivered to high level service. The boilers — two Daniel Adamson Cornish — have now been removed. A scheme for restoring the engine to steam using a small gas-fired boiler has been considered.

Access is by application to the Folkestone & District Water Co, Cherry Garden Lane, Folkestone, Kent, CT19 4QB.

ELDER & WATSON, Strathaven, Lanark

SINGLE CYLINDER HORIZONTAL MILL ENGINE
Elder & Watson Ltd, Strathaven, Lanark Maker and date obscure, 10 in × 18 in, slide valve, trunk crosshead-guides, disc crank, Pickering governor, flywheel 6 ft diameter. Cornish boiler, Wilson Boilers, Lilybank Works, Glasgow, 1895, hand fired, Boston Marine Patent smoke-burning furnace, 50 psi.

Reputedly made by Crawhall & Campbell in the 1850s the engine is undoubtedly old and the cylinder is unlagged. Installed here second hand in 1900 the Pickering governor may well be this date. The trunk crosshead-guide is a separate casting, bored out and then bolted to the flat table-like bedplate. The marine type big-end is a typical Scottish touch. Drive to the mill was by flat belt from a pulley mounted alongside the flywheel. The Cornish boiler is still in use providing process steam and heating in winter.

This engine is privately preserved and access is by prior application.

ELLESMERE PORT CANAL DOCKS,
Manchester Ship Canal Company, Cheshire

TWIN CYLINDER HORIZONTAL PUMPING ENGINES (2)
Sir W. G. Armstrong & Co, Newcastle-upon-Tyne, 1873.
INVERTED VERTICAL TWIN TANDEM PUMPING ENGINE
Frank Pearn & Co, Ltd, Manchester, c1910
INVERTED VERTICAL TWIN CYLINDER PUMPING ENGINE
John Cameron, Manchester.
INVERTED VERTICAL SINGLE CYLINDER DONKEY PUMP
John Cameron, Manchester, (transferred from Lower Station).

Hydraulic machinery was extensively used in the nineteenth century for powering dockside cranes, lock gates etc. At Ellesmere Port two hydraulic power stations were built, known as the Upper and Lower Stations respectively. The Upper Station is now in the care of the North Western Museum of Inland Navigation and the plant and buildings are undergoing extensive restoration. For this reason the station is not accessible for viewing at present.

It is the intention to restore the plant to working order and when this is complete it should form an impressive preserved installation.

Elder & Watson. The flywheel with light spokes and the unlagged cylinder are indicative of great age. Note also the separate bored trunk guide and marine type big-end.

ELLENROAD RING MILL,
New Hey, Rochdale, Lancs

TWIN TANDEM COMPOUND MILL ENGINE
J. & W. McNaught, Rochdale, 1892, rebuilt by
Clayton, Goodfellow & Co Ltd, Blackburn,
1921, Corliss valves HP, piston valves LP,
flywheel 28 ft diameter grooved for forty-eight
ropes, 2,500 hp, 58½ rpm, 180 psi.

This engine was built for the Ellenroad
Spinning Co's new mill as a twin tandem
triple-expansion with Corliss valves on the HP
cylinder and piston valves on all the others.
Running at 55 rpm the indicated horse-power
was 1,800 and the engine drove 122,000 mule
spindles.

The mill was all but destroyed by a fire in
1920, and as the name now implies ring
spinning was adopted in the rebuilt mill. To
increase the power of the engine it was rebuilt
as a straight twin-tandem compound by replacing the original HP and IP cylinders with
two HP cylinders, each of which exhausted to
one of the original LP cylinders. The flywheel
was renewed and made wider than the original
which had carried forty-five ropes.

In 1975 electrification of the mill drives was
completed and the engine, by now the last in
the Lancashire cotton spinning trade, was
taken out of use. From 1971 it had run as a
single tandem compound with one side disconnected to maintain as much efficiency as
possible on the reduced loadings as electrification progressed. The engine was maintained
in working order after cessation of work and in
1978 all dismantled parts were restored. From
time to time the engine is run under steam.

Access is by prior application to the mill.

*Ellenroad Ring Mill. When Clayton, Goodfellow
fitted new HP cylinders to the J. & W. Mc-
Naught engine, as usual they used Craig's cut-off
gear for the Corliss valves. The original LP
cylinders with piston valves were retained.*

ELLIOT COLLIERY EAST PIT,
New Tredegar, Glamorgan

> TWIN TANDEM COMPOUND COLLIERY
> WINDING ENGINE
> Thornewill & Warham, Burton-on-Trent,
> 1891, rebuilt 1904, 28 in (HP), 42 in (LP) ×
> 72 in stroke, Corliss valves HP, Cornish valves
> LP, 'Diabolo' winding drum 15 ft to 26 ft
> diameter, post brakes, 160 psi.

Built as a twin-cylinder simple engine the
tandem high-pressure cylinders were added
when higher pressure boilers were installed,
the new cylinders then exhausting into the
originals. The diabolo drum also replaced a
parallel drum of 24 ft diameter. Today the
engine is the only Thornewill & Warham
winding engine preserved and is a large one for
this maker. Also it appears to be the only
surviving engine with a diabolo drum, although this type of drum was once quite
extensively used. Unfortunately the engine is
not accessible at the present time, but it is in
the care of the National Museum of Wales who
have plans to motorise it and in due course
place it on public display.

ELSECAR COLLIERY,
Elsecar, Barnsley, S Yorks

> ATMOSPHERIC BEAM PUMPING ENGINE
> Maker unknown, 1795, 48 in diameter cyl-
> inder, drop valves, plug-rod valve-gear, twin-
> plate cast-iron beam, parallel motion.

This engine is now the sole surviving
Newcomen-type engine in its original location,
and it has had a remarkable working career.
Although the engine house is dated 1787 the
engine dates from 1795. It is another example
of the atmospheric-type engine installed at a
colliery after the proven success of the Watt
separate-condenser engine. As built the cylinder was 42 in bore and the larger cylinder
was fitted in 1801. The original wooden beam
remained until 1836 when replacement by the
present cast-iron beam was made. The present
valves and valve gear were also probably fitted
at this time. From 1836 the engine worked
continuously until 1923 and then occasionally
until 1930. The 1836 beam has parallel motion
for both piston and pump rods, not a unique
feature but rare on a mine pumping engine.

The engine remained in its original state
regarding method of operation. Injection was
always direct into the cylinder and no refine-
ment of a pickle pot condenser was fitted. As
preserved the pump rods, save for the top
section above ground level, have been cut away
and the engine is held outdoors by a system of
weights.

For access application must be made to the
National Coal Board, Barnsley Area, Grime-
thorpe, S Yorkshire.

ETRUSCAN BONE MILL,
Etruria, Stoke-on-Trent

> SINGLE CYLINDER BEAM ENGINE
> Probably Sherratt of Salford, c1839, 30 in ×
> 60 in.

Installed at the bone works second-hand in
1858 the engine worked until 1972. The
makers were early builders of steam engines
and made an engine for an experimental steam
tug on the Bridgewater Canal. Preserved with
the engine is a single-cylinder inverted vertical
rotative pump.

The site is now under the care of Stoke-on-
Trent City Museum and restoration of buildings, grinding pans and engine is proceeding.
Occasional open days are held until the work is
completed; further details from the museum.

FELSTOR LTD,
Manor Brickworks, Raunds, Northants

> SINGLE CYLINDER SEMI-PORTABLE
> OVERTYPE ENGINE
> William Foster & Co Ltd, Lincoln, 1942,
> 50 hp.

A late engine for the conventional 'open crank'
type and even more interesting because it is a
semi-portable. The maker is one of the Eastern
England builders and in this case perhaps
better known for traction engines.

Application should be made to the firm for
access.

FENLAND LAUNDRIES,
Belton Lane, Grantham, Lincs

> SINGLE CYLINDER HORIZONTAL MILL
> ENGINE
> Marshall, Sons & Co Ltd, Gainsborough,
> 1912.

A remarkable instance of private preservation
in situ for the engine ceased work in 1946. It is
still workable. Prior application should be
made to the laundry for access.

FERRANTI LTD, Hollinwood, Lancs

CROSS-COMPOUND INVERTED ENCLOSED
ENGINE
S. Z. de Ferranti Ltd, Hollinwood, 1900, No
381, 13in (HP), 28in (LP) × 13in stroke,
Fincke's valve gear, grid-iron slide valves
(separate for inlet and exhaust) Lumb's governor, 120rpm, 120psi.

S. Z. de Ferranti developed two designs for
engines to drive generators for the early power
stations. One of these designs had grid-iron
slide valves, and happily this example has
survived. In the inverted cross-compound
engine the generator virtually acted as the
flywheel and this layout was popular in the
early days of electricity supply. As these
engines were quickly outclassed by steam
turbines they generally had a short life, and
this engine survives because in 1920 it was sold
for use as a mill engine. A grooved flywheel was
substituted for the generator and the engine
was installed in a mill at Chorley, where it
drove conventionally by ropes to line-shafting.
Here it worked most reliably until closure of
the mill in 1952 whereupon it was dismantled
and re-erected at the Ferranti works. As

exhibited it is coupled to a Bruce Peebles
alternator by ropes.

It is likely that the speed of 120rpm dates
from the conversion to a mill engine. The
enclosed construction indicates a higher
original speed. A possibility is 167rpm corresponding to an alternating current frequency
of 50 cycles per second (Hertz) with a 36-pole
alternator. Apart from the valve gear and the
grid-iron valves an unusual feature is the twin-
bar design of the connecting rods. No doubt
this was another product of S. Z de Ferranti's
fertile brain.

Access is by application to the Archivist at
Ferranti Ltd, and may be restricted to parties.

*Ferranti Ltd. The Ferranti engine is full of
unusual features not least the separate slide
valves and valve chests for inlet and exhaust. As
displayed the engine is roped to a Bruce Peebles
alternator, which is not the original arrangement.*

FETTYKILL MILLS,
Smith, Anderson & Co Ltd, Leslie, Fife

SINGLE CYLINDER INVERTED VERTICAL
ENGINE
James Milne & Co Ltd, Edinburgh, 1897, 8 in
× 14 in, slide valve, hammer frame, disc crank.

Installed to drive a direct-current generator for
lighting the engine is now privately preserved.
Access is by application; the water turbines
and pass-out steam turbines which power the
mill are also of interest.

*Fettykil Paper Mills. James Milne inverted
vertical engine. The overhung disc crank gives the
engine an unusual appearance.*

FLEAM DYKE PUMPING STATION,
Cambridge

TANDEM COMPOUND WATERWORKS
PUMPING ENGINES (2)
Hathorn Davey & Co Ltd, Leeds, 1920, 23 in
(HP), 51 in (LP), × 48 in stroke, Corliss valves,
Porter-type governor, superheated steam
120 psi, 600°F, 200 rpm, two well pumps 165 ft
lift, double-acting force pump 45 psi, all driven
from tail rod.

This pumping station was started in 1914, but
completion was held up until 1920 due to
World War 1. The engines gave excellent
service and were in continuous use until 1976.
Steam was supplied by three John Thompson
Lancashire boilers with Green's economisers

*Fleam Dyke. There was plenty of metal in the
Hathorn Davey tandem compound engines. Note
the proportions of the engine bed and slide bars.
The engine was working when the photograph was
taken.*

and Sugden superheaters. During the early 1950s improvements were carried out, the engines being fitted with re-heaters between HP and LP stages. Larger superheaters were fitted to two boilers and these were also fitted with Hodgkinson low-ram coking stokers. To economise in steam usage engine-driven boiler-feed pumps were fitted to replace the Weir direct acting type, which had exhausted to atmosphere.

Viewing is by application to the Cambridge Water Company, Rustat Road, Cambridge.

GALE'S BREWERY, Horndean, Hampshire

> INVERTED VERTICAL ENGINES
> Plenty & Son, Newbury, c1870, twin cylinder $7\frac{1}{2}$ in × 9 in approx, slide valves, 80 rpm.
> Belliss & Morcom, Birmingham, single cylinder, enclosed, 7 in × 5 in, piston valve, 470 rpm.

The engines at Gale's — a 'real ale' brewery — have not been used for many years, but they are still in working order and are still run from time to time. The Plenty engine was built as a launch engine and was installed at the brewery second-hand about 1900. The reversing gear was removed, a flywheel from an even older engine was fitted, and a governor taken from a traction engine was rigged up. The Belliss & Morcom engine was nominally a replacement for the Plenty engine which, by good fortune, was never removed. Both engines drove lineshafting by belt.

GARLOGIE TWEED MILL, Aberdeen

> HOUSE BUILT SINGLE BEAM ENGINE
> Maker unknown, c1830s, 18 in × 48 in, slide valve, Watt-type governor, single plate cast-iron beam, cast-iron cruciform connecting rod, flywheel 16 ft diameter, jet condenser below floor.

A remarkable survival of a fine engine as it ceased work in 1904 and the mill which it drove has long been demolished. The engine is not preserved in the restored sense, but the engine house has been kept weatherproof although the inevitable pigeons have found a way in. The valve gear has been partly dismantled.

Access is not generally available and prior arrangement is necessary with The Factor, Dunecht Estate, Skene, Aberdeenshire.

THE GOLDEN LION, Southwick, Hants

> SINGLE CYLINDER HORIZONTAL ENGINE
> Maker unknown, c1860s, 6 in × 10 in, slide valve; vertical boiler, 1947, 80 psi.

Many years ago it was common for public houses to have their own brew house. The Golden Lion is now probably a unique example, although the engine is now out of use. It drove the brewhouse machinery by belt and lineshafting.

Ask at the pub for access.

HALL & WOODHOUSE BREWERY, Blandford St Mary, Dorset

> SINGLE CYLINDER HORIZONTAL ENGINES (2)
> Gimson & Co, Leicester, 1899, 12 in × 24 in, slide valve.
> Ruston, Proctor & Co Ltd, Lincoln, 1902

The Gimson engine is a working engine driving the brewery machinery and thus is not strictly a preserved engine. The Ruston engine was removed from the Skona brewery at Gillingham (Dorset) and re-erected at the Blandford brewery for preservation.

Access is by application to the brewery.

Garlogie Tweed Mill. General view of engine at driving floor level. The governor and cruciform connecting rod are typical of the period of manufacture. The valve gear has been dismantled for many years to allow access to the turbine house next door, and the lattice work eccentric rod is seen tied up vertically.

GLYN PITS, Pontypool, Gwent

SINGLE CYLINDER VERTICAL COLLIERY
WINDING ENGINE
Neath Abbey Ironworks, 1845, 36 in × 60 in,
flat ropes, two drums 15 ft diameter
SINGLE CYLINDER ROTATIVE BEAM
PUMPING ENGINE
Neath Abbey Ironworks, 1845, 36 in × 72 in,
single plate-beam, Cornish-type engine house.

The Glyn Pits engines lay derelict for many
years before being designated as an Industrial
Monument in 1974. The winding engine was
stopped in 1932. As yet no restoration has been
carried out and the engines are not available for
close inspection.

*Glyn Pits. Derelict engine house and Cornish-
type rotative engine which drove pumps through
reduction gearing from the crankshaft.* ▶

*Henwood. Cylinders, steam chest and parallel
motion linkage of Woolf compound engine No 2.* ▼

HENWOOD PUMPING STATION,
Ashford, Kent

WOOLF COMPOUND SINGLE COLUMN BEAM
ENGINES (2)
No 1: Thos Horn, Westminster, c1870, 8 in ×
18 in (HP), 14 in × 27 in (LP), slide valves,
Watt-type governor, single-plate cast-iron
beam, cruciform connecting rod, three-throw
well-pump gear drive.
No 2: Thos Horn & Son, London, 1885,
dimensions as No 1, forged connecting rod,
three-throw well pump, gear drive, hardwood
teeth.

Two very pleasant engines virtually identical
with minor differences indicative of the dates
of building. The cast-iron gearing of No 1
engine is probably a replacement, No 2 engine
retaining the original gearing with hardwood
mortised teeth. Often referred to as 'The
Chapel' the ecclesiastical atmosphere of the
engine house is heightened by the raised
platform and 'pulpit' for the officiating engineman.

Access is by arrangement with the Divisional
Manager of the Mid-Kent Water Company,
Ashford Division.

HOPWAS PUMPING STATION,
Tamworth, Staffs

SINGLE BEAM PUMPING ENGINES (2)
Gimson & Co, Leicester, 1879, 25 in × 60 in,
Meyer expansion slide valves, twin-plate cast-
iron beam, flywheel 12 ft diameter, ½ mgd,
260 ft head, 20 rpm, 50 hp, 40 psi.

The two engines remain for the time being in
unrestored condition as there may be doubt
about their future. Named *Woody* and *Spruce*
after Dr Woody and Mr Spruce, contemporary
local notables, the engines were built for the
Tamworth local authority. The design is neat
and robust and the engines gave excellent
service until replaced by electric pumps in
1962. Pumps were operated by the usual
wooden spears attached to a first section of iron
rods suspended from the beam. It is interesting
to compare these engines with the other Gimson survivors at Clay Mills and Leicester,
particularly in the progress of beam design
from cast-iron through wrought-iron to steel.

Access is by application to the South Staffordshire Waterworks Company, Engineer's
Office, Sheepcote Lane, Birmingham, B16
8AR.

*Hopwas. Cylinders of the Gimson engines Spruce
(left) and Woody (right). The expansion slide
valves are worked by eccentrics, rods and bell
cranks below floor.*

*Hopwas. The beam chamber. Compare the cast
iron beams of these engines with the later Gimson
engines at Clay Mills and Abbey Pumping
Station.*

KING & BARNES BREWERY, Bishopric, Horsham, Sussex

SINGLE CYLINDER HORIZONTAL ENGINES (2)
E. S. Hindley, Bourton, Dorset, 9 in × 9 in approx.
Hayward, Tyler, 6 in × 6 in approx.

Installed second hand about 1900 the Hindley engine was at work until recently. The Hayward, Tyler engine is preserved at the brewery, but is not in its working location.

Access is by application to the brewery.

LANGFORD PUMPING STATION, Essex

INVERTED VERTICAL TRIPLE EXPANSION
WATERWORKS PUMPING ENGINE
The Lilleshall Company, Oakengates, 1931.

One of two preserved Lilleshall triple-expansion waterworks engines, (the other being at Chelvey, Bristol Waterworks Co). The 1930s saw the last of new steam waterworks engines and it is creditable that this late example from Lilleshall has been preserved.

Application for access to Essex Water Company, 342 South Street, Romford, Essex, RM1 2AL.

LEIGH SPINNERS LTD, Leigh, Lancs

CROSS COMPOUND MILL ENGINE
Yates & Thom, Blackburn, 1925, named *Mayor* and *Mayoress*, 36 in (HP), 60 in (LP) × 60 in stroke, Corliss valves, Lumb's governor, girder bed, trunk crosshead guides, boarded flywheel grooved for forty-five ropes, 2,000 hp, twin cylinder inverted vertical barring engine.

Although the twin-tandem engine was very popular for the high powers required in the Lancashire cotton spinning mills, some very large cross-compound engines were also made. The largest had a low-pressure cylinder 73 in diameter. This engine is not quite as large, but it is of impressive size nonetheless. The horsepower should be treated with some reserve as spinning mill engines were often overloaded. The engine is of typical Yates & Thom design, with tail rods supported on slides and the underfloor condenser with air pump driven by rocker arm from the LP tail rod. Other features are the generally massive girder-bed construction and the use of Dobson's trip gear on the Corliss valves. The mill was converted from cotton spinning to carpet manufacture in 1971, but the engine was retained for a time to drive a stand-by generator.

Leigh Spinners. Mayor and Mayoress by Yates & Thom is now the largest surviving cross-compound mill engine. Note the tail rods and supporting slides.

LEVANT MINE, St Just, Cornwall

SINGLE BEAM WINDING ENGINE
Harvey & Co, Hayle, 1840, 24 in × 4 ft, equal beam, Cornish valves, gab valve gear.

The oldest engine in Cornwall, this whim or winding engine is of the 'all indoors' type quite often used in Cornish mining, but less familiar than the half outdoors pattern. Even so, the winding drum is still located outdoors. As built the engine had plug-rod valve-gear, but the engine ran away out of control about 1862 causing extensive damage. A new cylinder was required and the present gab valve-gear was then fitted, having a 'T' handle to work the valves when reversing. Originally the engine drew kibbles in the shaft, which was sunk adjacent to the existing pumping shaft, so that output could be increased. The winding speed was 150 feet per minute, winding being with chains. Further improvement was made about 1860 when skips running on guides were put in, with wire rope winding. As well as increasing the payload this enabled winding speed to be increased to 400 feet per minute.

After ceasing work with the closure of Levant Mine in 1930, the engine lay derelict until 1935, when it was purchased by the Cornish Engines Preservation Society as the first engine to be preserved in Cornwall. It is now in the care of the National Trust and may be visited by application to Geevor Tin Mines Ltd, St Just.

Levant Whim. General view of the cliff top whim engine house with the derelict pumping engine house nearby. The whim engine boiler was housed in a lean-to on the near side of the engine house, but this has been demolished. The skip shaft is still used for ventilating the Geevor Mine.

Levant Whim. Bottom chamber or driving floor. Unlike a great many all-indoor house-built engines there are no columns to give extra support under the beam trunnion bearings.

LITTLETON PUMPING STATION,
Staines, Surrey

UNIFLOW ENGINE & CENTRIFUGAL
WATERWORKS PUMP
Littleton Pumping Station, Nr Staines,
Thames Water Authority
Worthington-Simpson Ltd, Newark-on-
Trent, 1923, 28 in × 39 in, drop valves, 132 rpm,
800 hp, superheated steam 190 psi, direct-
coupled centrifugal pump, 75 mgd, 30 ft head.
Lighting Set: Inverted-vertical compound en-
closed engine, Ashworth & Parker, Bury, 1924,
piston valves, 450 rpm, Lancashire Dynamo
DC generator, 25 kW, 210 volts, 119 amps.

First devised by Jacob Perkins, an American
living in London around 1827, the Uniflow
design was finally perfected in 1908 by Professor Stumpf of Berlin, and became the most
efficient form of reciprocating steam engine to
be produced. Steam is cut off very early in the
stroke and the whole of the expansion takes
place in one cylinder. Condensation losses are
minimised by exhausting through ports at the
centre of the cylinder barrel, these being
covered and uncovered by the piston at each
stroke.

Access is by application to the Thames
Water Authority, Metropolitan Division, New
River Head, London, EC1R 4IP.

Littleton. Where waterworks pumping required large quantity rather than high head centrifugal pumps were ideal. To make a compact and highly efficient installation the pump was coupled directly to a Uniflow engine.

Littleton. Ashworth & Parker high speed compound engine and DC generator, which provided current for electric lighting.

LONGLANDS FARM,
Holkham Estate, Wells-next-the-Sea, Norfolk

SEMI-PORTABLE SINGLE CYLINDER
OVERTYPE ENGINE
Longlands Farm, Holkham Estate, Nr Wells-
next-the-Sea.
Richard Garrett & Sons, Leiston, 1914, No
32587, 8½in × 13in, piston valve, expansion
valve gear, centrifugal crankshaft governor,
flywheel 4ft 3in diameter, Cornish multi-
tubular boiler, superheater, 190psi, 65hp
(approx), 200rpm

This is a design aimed primarily at the overseas
and Colonial markets. The boiler has bolted
front and tube plates to allow complete access
to the interior parts of the boiler for cleaning
and repair; this was a useful feature where
available feed water was of poor quality. The
expansion valve gear and superheater give
maximum possible economy on this otherwise
simple unit and the relatively high working
pressure for a single-cylinder engine will be
noted. The centrifugal governor on the crankshaft was a common feature on 'Colonial'
engines as it was difficult to tamper with. It
was also used on Colonial-type traction
engines.

Longlands Farm. Garrett semi-portable engin
(called semi-stationary by the makers). Ofte
known as locomobiles the type has a removabl
boiler front plate. A section of the smoke bo
tubeplate could also be unbolted allowing firebo
and tubes to be withdrawn from the boiler shell

The Longlands engine drove the estate sawmill and blacksmith's shop until 1963 and it
was in sawmilling that the semi-portable
engine probably saw its greatest use in the UK.
Needing only a supply of fuel and water and a
level base to stand on it was easy to install with
a minimum of skilled labour. At the present
time the engine is unrestored but it is intended
in due course to renovate the engine and make
available for public inspection. For the
moment access is only available by application
to the Estate Office.

LOUND PUMPING STATION,
Lowestoft, Suffolk

SINGLE CYLINDER GRASSHOPPER
WATERWORKS PUMPING ENGINES (2)
Easton & Amos, London, c1854, 15in × 24in.

Grasshopper beam engines were more compact than the conventional beam engine and
were popular in the mid-nineteenth century
for all kinds of duties involving low powers.
The Lound engines are excellently preserved
examples of the type as applied to waterworks

pumping, and here they drove three-throw
pumps. One of the engines is motorised so tha
it can be turned over for demonstratio
purposes.
Access is by application to the East Anglia
Water Company, 163, High Street, Lowestoft
Suffolk.

LOW HALL FARM SEWAGE WORKS,
Walthamstow, London

TWIN CYLINDER HORIZONTAL ENGINE
Marshall, Sons & Co Ltd, Gainsborough
c1896.

What were otherwise standard 'mill' engines
were from time to time used for drivin
centrifugal pumps by belt or ropes from th
flywheel. In sewage works such an arrange
ment could be used for storm water pumps
making an installation cheap in first cost, im
portant when the plant saw only occasional us
during the course of a year.
Access is by application to the Londo
Borough of Waltham Forest, Department o
Cleansing & Transport, Low Hall Depot, Lo
Hall Lane, London, E17.

LUMBHOLE MILL,
Kettleshulme, Cheshire

HOUSE-BUILT SINGLE BEAM ENGINE &
WATERWHEEL
c1835, 18in × 52in, slide valve, Watt-type
governor, single-plate cast-iron beam, cruciform connecting rod. Cornish boiler externally
fired. Low breast waterwheel 25ft diameter ×
6ft wide, 38hp.

Lumbhole Mill was built for the manufacture
of candle wicks in the 1820s being then a two
storey building. It burnt down in the early
1830s and was then rebuilt to its present three
storey form. The surviving power plant, except
for the boiler, probably dates from this re-
construction. On the steam chest cover is a
plate 'J. & E. Arnfield, New Mills', which most
likely indicates the maker of a replacement
cylinder. This firm still exists, now trading at
Audenshaw.

It was once common to instal a steam engine
to assist a waterwheel, either as supplementary
power, or to take over completely in times of
drought. Here a dog clutch is provided to
engage or disengage the engine drive. The
waterwheel is entirely within the mill building
and is of all-metal construction. The axle is
square section with turned journals. The boiler
was installed about 1890 and probably replaced a wagon-top boiler. The furnace is
below the boiler shell and the gases pass under
the boiler to the rear, where they are returned
to the front, through what would normally be
the furnace tube. At the front of the boiler the
gases divide in a brick flue and pass down each
side of the boiler, before escaping to the
chimney.

Lumbhole Mill. The beam chamber. There is a ▲
notable lack of safety fencing.

*Lumbhole Mill. View from the packing platform.
The geared connection to the water-wheel is on
the other side of the engine house wall.*

Lumbhole Mill. The waterwheel is housed entirely within the mill building. Drive to the mill shaft is from an integral gear ring on the rim. Note the square shaft with only the journals turned.

MAPLE BROOK PUMPING STATION,
Burntwood, Lichfield, Staffs

INVERTED VERTICAL TRIPLE EXPANSION PUMPING ENGINE
W. & J. Galloway, Manchester, 1913, 22 in (HP), 35 in (IP), 55 in (LP) × 48 in stroke, Corliss valves, two flywheels 14 ft diameter, 20 rpm, 225 ihp, 160 psi.

This is the only Galloway pumping engine to survive in Britain. Pumping was from a well 270 ft deep. Superheated steam was used and although drop valves are usually associated with superheat there were very many installations where Corliss valve engines gave long and reliable service. For slow speed waterworks pumping the inverted vertical triple expansion engine represented the ultimate development and high efficiencies were achieved.

Access is by application to the South Staffordshire Waterworks Company, Engineer's Office, Sheepcote Street, Birmingham, B16 8AR.

NO 1 PUMPING STATION,
Duncrue Street, Belfast

HORIZONTAL CROSS-COMPOUND ENGINES (2) & CENTRIFUGAL PUMPS
Victor Coates & Co Ltd, Belfast, c1886, 12⅜ in (HP), 21 in (LP) × 36 in stroke, slide valves, flywheel 13 ft diameter with twelve ropes, 74 rpm, 100 psi. Two Worthington-Simpson centrifugal pumps.

The last steam-driven sewage pumping plant to remain in service in the UK, it was only replaced by electric plant in 1979. When installed the engines drove ram pumps, but these were later replaced by centrifugal pumps, each engine driving two pumps by ropes from the flywheel. Storm water was dealt with by four additional centrifugal pumps, two with electric drive and two steam driven. Each of the latter was direct coupled to a 17½ in × 15 in W. H. Allen single-cylinder engine. Steam was supplied to the whole plant by a range of six Lancashire boilers made by Victor Coates and supplied with their engines. A Green's economiser was fitted in the main flue.

To view, prior permission must be obtained from the Divisional Water Manager, Department of the Environment for Northern Ireland, Water Service-Eastern Division, 1 Donegall Square North, Belfast, BT1 5GE.

OWSTON FERRY PUMPING STATION,
South Axholme Drainage Board, Lincs

TANDEM COMPOUND ENGINE &
CENTRIFUGAL PUMP
Marshall & Sons, Gainsborough, 1910, No
52767, 7 in (HP), 13 in (LP) × 20 in stroke, drop
valves, high speed governor, girder bed, trunk
crosshead guides, disc crank, 140 rpm centrifugal pump Drysdale & Co, Glasgow,
20,000 gpm. Two Cornish boilers, Marshall &
Sons, 1910, Nos 52765 & 52766, 150 psi.
Ramsbottom safety valves, single-cylinder
wall-mounted 'Mumford' boiler-feed pump.

This engine is one of two installed to drain
fenland and lift into the River Trent. A Ruston
diesel engine replaced one engine in 1952 and
this engine was itself replaced in 1964 by a
Blackstone diesel-pump set, but fortunately
allowed to remain in situ.

It is a later engine than the one at Gladstone
Pottery, and of a type given much publicity by
Marshalls. The valves are operated from a
geared layshaft with eccentrics and rods
actuating the HP inlet valves and having
governor controlled trip gear. All other valves
are actuated by rods and cam and roller gear.
This form of valve gear made the engine
eminently suitable for relatively high speed
and enabled the centrifugal pump to be directly coupled to the crankshaft. The cylinders are
steam jacketted, steam traps being fitted to
drain away condensate. Exhaust steam from
the LP cylinder passes to a condenser below

*Owston Ferry. A simple, but neat, housing for fen
drainage pumps. The extension on the right dates
from 1964 and accommodates a Blackstone diesel
engine.*

floor level, the air pump being driven by an
eccentric on the crankshaft, the pump rod
passing vertically downwards through the
floor. The boilers, fitted with enormous Ramsbottom safety valves, are typical Marshall type.
Stand-by boiler feed is (or was) by an injector.

Access is by application to the South
Axholme Drainage Board, Market Place,
Epworth, Lincs.

*Owston Ferry. This tandem compound is probab-
ly the most delightful survivor of all Marshall
engines.*

PARKANDILLICK CLAYWORKS,
St Austell, Cornwall

CORNISH PUMPING ENGINE
Sandys, Vivian & Co, Copperhouse Foundry, Hayle, 1852, 50 in × 10/9 ft, twin-plate cast-iron beam, twin-plug rods, two cataracts.

The Cornish mining industry declined just as the china clay industry was expanding. Many of the smaller pumping engines from closed mines found new employment pumping clay-bearing water from the clay pits. The Parkandillick engine was built for Old Sump Shaft, Wheal Kitty Mine, St Agnes and was already 60 years old when re-erected at Parkandillick in 1912. A new cylinder was provided at this time by Bartle's Foundry, Carn Brae, but the rest of the engine seems to have been original.

The arrangement of the top nozzles differs from usual in that the valves are arranged with the equilibrium valve in the centre instead of at the end of the nozzle chamber. This appears to have been a feature of the smaller Copperhouse Foundry engines, where a single perpendicular pipe was used to convey equilibrium steam. The design of the steam passage ways was simplified, but it meant that inlet steam had to come into contact with the walls of passages and nozzles which conveyed relatively cool equilibrium steam, and this must have meant some loss of thermal efficiency. There are two cataracts so that the engine paused at the end of both indoor and outdoor strokes. This engine worked for over a hundred years and is now part of the Wheal Martyn china clay industry museum scheme. It is now demonstrated on low pressure compressed air.

Access is by application to English Clays Lovering Pochin & Co Ltd, John Keay House, St Austell, Cornwall.

Parkandillick Clayworks. General view of the engine house with its lean-to boiler house alongside. The chimney is typically Cornish but, has unfortunately lost its brick upper section.

Parkandillick Clayworks. Valve gear, perpendicular pipe and bottom nozzle. The piston is at the top of its stroke and the tappet on the nearest plug rod has engaged the 'top handle' and closed the equilibrium valve by rotating the middle arbor.

◀ *Parkandillick Clayworks. Indoor end of the beam of the Sandys, Vivian Cornish pumping engine.*

PRINCES DRIVE SEWAGE PUMPING STATION, Leamington Spa, Warwickshire

DUPLEX TANDEM TRIPLE EXPANSION PUMPING ENGINE Worthington-Simpson Ltd, Newark-on-Trent, 1918

The Worthington Duplex arrangement achieved considerable success in waterworks pumping applications, and could also be applied to sewage pumping. This engine worked until 1965. Also preserved at the station is a Belliss & Morcom inverted vertical high-speed enclosed compound engine, which dates from 1928 and ran until steam ceased at the station about 1965.

Access is by application to the Severn-Trent Water Authority, Avon Division, Waveley Road, Coventry, CV1 3AJ.

PORT OF BRISTOL AUTHORITY, Underfall Yard Workshops, Bristol

TWIN CYLINDER HORIZONTAL ENGINE Tangyes, Birmingham, 1885, 8 in × 16 in
VERTICAL SINGLE CYLINDER ENGINE John Cameron, Manchester, 1885. Drove a punching and shearing machine.
INVERTED VERTICAL SINGLE CYLINDER PUMP A. G. Mumford, Colchester, c1885.
STEAM HAMMER Maker unknown, c1885.

Access to the workshops is by application to the Port of Bristol Authority, Harbour Master's and Engineer's Dept, Bristol.

PRINCES WHARF, Bristol

35-ton HEAVY LIFT CRANE Stothert & Pitt, 1875.

The crane has separate engines for lifting and slewing. Steam is provided by a Marshall vertical boiler 10 ft high by 4 ft 6 in diameter. The City of Bristol Museums have the crane in their care and it is operated under steam from time to time. Details from City of Bristol, Museum & Art Gallery, Queen's Road, Bristol 8.

Ram Brewery. Driving floor view of 1835 engine. The cruciform section cast-iron connecting rod is well evident.

RAM BREWERY, Young & Co, Wandsworth, London

WOOLF COMPOUND A-FRAME MILL ENGINES (2) Wentworth & Son, Wandsworth, 1835, rebuilt 1863, 9 in × 30 in (HP), 15 in × 42 in (LP), slide valves, Porter governor, single-plate cast-iron beam, cruciform connecting rod, bevel-gear drive to vertical main shaft. Wentworth & Son, Wandsworth, 1867, generally as above, Watt-type governor.

Although these engines are still in use to drive the brewery machinery, there must be some degree of preservation involved in the continued survival of such engines. The 1835 engine is certainly the oldest engine in commercial use in the UK and possibly in the world. The 1835 engine was 'altered' from 12 hp to 16 hp in 1863 according to the maker's plate, but the precise nature of the alteration is not known. The Woolf-compound form is believed to be original and Wentworth was thus early in the use of the compound principle.

Prior application is necessary for access.

ROALL PUMPING STATION,
Eggborough, Yorks

WOOLF COMPOUND A-FRAME WATERWORKS
PUMPING ENGINE
Easton & Anderson, Erith, 1891, 14 in × 36 in
(HP), 20 in × 48 in (LP), Meyer expansion slide
valve (HP), simple slide valve (LP), twin-plate
cast-iron beam, flywheel 12 ft diameter,
20 rpm, 65 hp (approx).

This is a relatively small engine, typical of the
installations once common for supplying small
towns, and which were often built for the local
municipal authority. The Roall station was
originally the Pontefract Waterworks. The two
engines originally installed here pumped from
a common well the pumps being driven from
the indoor end of the beams. The cylinders are
supported by a framing over the well head. The
cylinders are lagged with polished-wood strips
secured by brass bands. A linkage from the
beam operates the rider valve of the Meyer
slide valve on the HP cylinder and a hand
adjustment is provided. The main valve is
operated by eccentric and rod from the crankshaft and this valve gear also operates the LP
slide valve.

Access is by application to the Yorkshire
Water Authority, South Eastern Division,
Copley House, Waterdale, Doncaster,
S Yorks.

Roall (top). Easton's & Anderson A-frame
Woolf compound beam engine. The entablature is
supported by four slender columns from the bed-
plate.

Roall (bottom). Neat wood lagging and the
different diameters and strokes of the Woolf
compound cylinders are clearly evident. The
piston rod glands have metallic packing, as
indicated by their large size.

RUNTLINGS MILL, Ossett, W Yorks

TANDEM COMPOUND HORIZONTAL MILL
ENGINE
Marsden's Engines Ltd, Heckmondwike,
1907, named *Rhoda*, 12 in (HP), 23 in (LP) ×
42 in stroke, Corliss valves (HP), slide valve
(LP), jet condenser (above floor), flywheel
grooved for six ropes, 82 rpm, 250 hp.

Now owned by the Oakliffe Engineering Co
Ltd, Runtlings Mill was until 1976 a shoddy
mill. Shoddy is wool reconstituted from old
garments. The old cloth is washed, finely
shredded and then re-spun; it can then be re-
woven into a low quality cloth and used for
Army blankets, carpet underlays etc. This is a
good example of the medium-sized engines
that abounded in the Yorkshire woollen industry. With the condenser behind the LP
cylinder and the air pump driven by the LP tail
rod, all parts except the boiler feed-pump are
above floor level. The feed pump is below the
floor driven by an eccentric and a vertical rod
from the crankshaft. The Corliss valve gear of
the claw type is particularly neat and its design

is typical Marsden. Marsden's built many
engines for the Yorkshire woollen trade and
this is the only one of theirs preserved.
Access is by application to the owners of
Runtlings Mill.

*Runtlings Mill. Generally the Yorkshire woollen
trade used less power than the cotton trade in
Lancashire, and moderately powered engines as
this Marsden tandem compound were once common. Simplicity and a considerable degree of
economy were achieved by the use of Corliss
valves on the HP cylinder and a slide valve on the
LP.*

Sandfields. Beam of the Cornish-type engine built by J. & G. Davies. The beam plates are closely spaced with centre rib and the parallel motion loops outside, features often found on engines built outside Cornwall.

SANDFIELDS PUMPING STATION, Lichfield

CORNISH PUMPING ENGINE
Jonah & George Davies, Tipton, 1873, 65 in × 9 ft equal beam, twin-plate cast-iron beam, twin plug-rods, two cataracts, 2 mgd, 355 ft head, 7 spm.

Carefully preserved at a still active, but now electrically operated, pumping station the engine house atmosphere is as near as can be simulated to that of 1873. Lighting is by 'oil effect' lamps and gives some idea of the level of illumination under which this and other engines of the time had to be operated. The engine itself shows some variations from true Cornish practice, the obvious one being that the beam plates are narrowly spaced with the parallel-motion loops outside. On the valve gear the steam arbor and horn are at the bottom and the top handle or equilibrium arbor is literally at the top on this engine. The cataracts are below the floor and are of the normal mine engine type as opposed to the ornamental waterworks type placed in full view above floor level. As preserved one cataract is disconnected and quite possibly the engine ran in this state latterly.

Access is by application to the South Staffordshire Waterworks Company, Engineer's Office, Sheepcote Lane, Birmingham, B16 8AR.

Sandfields. The valve gear which has the steam arbor at the bottom. Operation is by twin plug rods. The hand wheel controls the governor valve.

142

SHORE ROAD PUMPING STATION,
Birkenhead, Merseyside

COMPOUND NON-ROTATIVE GRASSHOPPER
BEAM PUMPING ENGINE
Andrew Barclay Sons & Co, Kilmarnock,
1884, 36in × 10ft (HP), 55in × 13ft (LP),
8spm, 70psi.

Installed to drain the Mersey Railway tunnel
under the river, the engine was not taken out of
commission until 1959, latterly being a stand-
by unit. More familiar perhaps as industrial
locomotive builders, Andrew Barclay's had a
considerable market in stationary engines,
principally in the mining industry.

The Shore Road engine is owned by British
Rail (London Midland Region), but it is not
generally accessible for viewing.

SOLWAY FLOUR MILLS, Silloth, Cumbria

HORIZONTAL CROSS COMPOUND MILL
ENGINE
Carels Freres, Ghent, Belgium, No 801 of
1904, 600mm (HP), 950mm (LP) × 1,500mm
stroke, double-beat drop valves, girder bed,
trunk crosshead guides, 18ft 6in flywheel
grooved for twenty ropes, steam at 160psi
superheated to 560°F, 65rpm, 750hp.

INVERTED VERTICAL HIGH SPEED ENCLOSED
ENGINE & DIRECT CURRENT GENERATOR
Belliss & Morcom compound engine, piston
valves, centrifugal crankshaft governor operating throttle valve. Mather & Platt DC generator, 80kW, 210 volts, 600 rpm. Engine No
6682.

Around the turn of the century Continental
makers were building highly economical drop-
valve engines. Against very strong local com-
petition Carels supplied a number of large
engines to Lancashire mills, none of which
survive, and this smaller engine to Solway
which happily does so. The engine is very
typical of Continental practice of the time. The
valves are fitted in the cylinder end-covers.
Operation is by geared layshaft on each side of
the engine. The HP inlet valves are driven
from eccentrics keyed to the layshaft with
governor controlled trip gear. All other valves
are operated by cams on the layshafts. Exhaust
from both engines passed to a surface condenser with an electrically driven W.H. Allen
air pump. In emergency exhaust could be
turned to atmosphere. Cooling water was

*Solway Flour Mills. Belliss & Morcom DC
generating set, itself quite a period piece.*

circulated by a Weir steam pump, now removed. Steam was supplied by three water-
tube boilers, now replaced.

Access is by arrangement with Carr's Flour
Mills Ltd, Solway Mills, Silloth, Cumbria.

143

SOUTH CROFTY MINE, Pool, Cornwall

CORNISH PUMPING ENGINE
ROBINSON'S 80 INCH
Sandy's, Vivian & Co, Copperhouse Foundry,
Hayle, 1854, 80 in × 10 ft equal beam, twin plug
rods, twin perpendicular pipes, 310 gpm, 337
fathoms, 5½ spm, 50 psi.

Designed by Samuel Grose, this engine like
most Cornish mine engines worked at several
locations during its career. It came to South
Crofty in 1903 from Tregurtha Downs Mine,
to pump in the then new Robinson's Shaft.
Unlike most of the earlier Cornish mine shafts,
this was truly vertical. Samuel Grose was in the
forefront of contemporary Cornish engine
designers, and in pursuit of maximum efficiency this engine is fitted with widely separ-
ated top nozzles. The inlet nozzle is at the
rear of the cylinder, diametrically opposite the
equilibrium nozzle. The aim of this was to
provide separate ports for inlet and equil-

*Solway Flour Mills. A Continental cross com-
pound by Carels Freres of Ghent, 1904, with drop
valves and a very neat outline. The valves are
driven by eccentrics and short rods from a lay
shaft. The valves are fitted in the cylinder end
covers to keep clearance volume to a minimum
and the valves rotate at each lift to equalise wear.*

ibrium steam thereby reducing temperature
fluctuations and condensation. Hocking &
Loam also designed engines at this period with
separate nozzles and the Prestongrange 70
inch is an example. There however the top
nozzles although separate are side-by-side.

At South Crofty the 80 inch did sterling
work and the cylinder cover was lifted only
twice from 1903 until the engine ceased work
in May 1955. It was the last Cornish engine to
work on a Cornish mine. The engine is in the
care of the National Trust, but South Crofty is
still a very busy and productive mine. For this
reason access is usually restricted to occasional
organised parties.

SPRINGHEAD PUMPING STATION,
Kingston-upon-Hull, Yorks

CORNISH WATERWORKS PUMPING ENGINE
Bells, Lightfoot & Co, Newcastle-on-Tyne, 1876, 90 in × 11 ft equal beam, wrought-iron beam, twin plug-rods, twin cataracts, two lift pumps in well 22 ft diameter × 73 ft deep, one plunger pump to variable head high-level service, 12 spm, 6¾ mgd.

The Springhead engine has a box girder beam — the strongest form possible. Of necessity the parallel-motion loops are outside the beam plates. The cylinder is neatly lagged with polished wood strips, but there is no steam case. The three top nozzles are in a cast-iron chest and twin perpendicular pipes convey equilibrium steam. The cataracts stand above floor level near the valve gear. In normal waterworks manner the beam trunnions are supported by a cast-iron entablature. Condenser, air pump and boiler-feed pump are under the floor and driven by rods from the outdoor end of the beam. The pumping arrangements are most interesting. The well pumps deliver to a tank near the well head, from which the plunger pump delivers to high level service. The forcing weight on the pump rod is a cast-iron tank which was filled or otherwise with water depending on the delivery head against the pump.

The engine is maintained in excellent condition as a static exhibit. Access is by arrangement with the Division Director, Yorkshire Water Authority, Eastern Division, Essex House, Manor St, Kingston-upon-Hull. There are many other interesting exhibits also at Springhead.

Springhead. (top). The forcing weight could be filled with water when it was required to pump to a higher head.

Springhead (bottom). The Grecian arch effect of the top nozzles and perpendicular pipes is particularly spectacular.

St Mary's Mill, Chalford, Glos

SIDE-BY-SIDE COMPOUND HORIZONTAL
MILL ENGINE
Tangye & Co Ltd, Birmingham, c1897, 13in
(HP), 25in (LP) × 24in stroke, slide valves,
Tangye & Johnson Patent cut-off on HP,
Porter governor, flywheel 11ft 3in diameter,
grooved for eight ropes, jet condenser, 160hp,
90rpm.

St Mary's Mill, built in the eighteenth century,
has seen many uses but for many years it has
been used for the manufacture of walking
sticks. It was originally powered by two large
waterwheels, but a beam engine made by
George Waller of Stroud was later installed in a
brick engine house at the side of the mill. A lack
of water led to reorganisation of the power
installation and the purchase of this engine in
1903. It was obtained by the Chalford Stick
Company from the Excelsior Engineering Co
and erected in a room adjacent to one of the
waterwheels, which was subsequently removed. The erection involved some ingenuity
and the engine embraces a cast-iron pillar
between bedplate and LP eccentric rod. Later
a defect in the mill shaft meant that the
flywheel had to be shifted along the crankshaft nearer to the engine bed. This fouled the
governor linkage to the cut-off gear and the
governor was altered to operate a butterfly

valve in the engine steam-pipe.

Designed for 125psi working pressure the
engine was steamed at St Mary's Mill by a
Lancashire boiler made by Foster of Preston in
1897 and installed in the old beam-engine
house. The engine ran until about 1958 and the
mill was purchased by the present owner in
1964. This compact engine is quite a large
example of what is now a very rare type. In
typical Tangye manner the cylinders are overhung from the bedplate which is flat with flat
slides for the crossheads. This is in contrast
with the well known Tangye single-cylinder
designs having girder bed and trunk
crosshead-guides.

The owner of St Mary's Mill, Mr George
Reynolds, is always pleased to show interested
visitors into the engine house and access
should be arranged by contacting him, phone:
045 388 2392. A scheme is in hand to install a
locomotive-type boiler to enable the engine to
be run for demonstration purposes.

*St Mary's Mill. The side-by-side compound
layout gave a very compact engine, but mill
engines of this design are now rare. This Tangye
engine ran at 90rpm, but higher speeds were
perhaps more usual. The smaller HP cylinder is
fitted with Tangye-Johnson expansion slide
valves. Control was by a Porter type governor but
this has been altered to operate a throttle valve.*

STOTHERT & PITT LTD, Bath

SINGLE CYLINDER BEAM ENGINE
Stothert & Pitt, 1866, 12 in × 18 in

One of the firm's own products, the engine has been brought back to the works and re-erected for preservation.

Prior application should be made to the firm for access.

TOLLEMACH & COBBOLD BREWERIES LTD, Cliff Brewery, Ipswich, Suffolk

HORIZONTAL TANDEM COMPOUND ENGINE
E. R. & F. Turner Ltd, Ipswich, No 1967, 12 in (HP), 16 in (LP) × 16 in stroke approx, Meyer expansion slide-valve HP, simple slide-valve LP, jet condenser.

Moderate power requirements did not necessarily mean that the simplest possible engine was installed, and small compound engines such as this were once in frequent use, but the survivors are very few. In this instance although the engine had been out of use for some years it was restored to working order in 1979. E. R. & F. Turner were well known in East Anglia principally as makers of flour milling machinery.

Access is by application to the brewery.

TRENCHERFIELD MILL, Courtaulds Ltd, Wigan, Lancs

TWIN TANDEM TRIPLE EXPANSION MILL ENGINE
John & Edward Wood, Bolton, 1907, $25\frac{1}{8}$ in (HP), $40\frac{1}{8}$ in (IP), (2) $44\frac{1}{4}$ in (LP) × 60 in stroke, Corliss valves, Lumb's governor, flywheel 26 ft 6 in diameter grooved for fifty-four ropes, 68 rpm, 2,500 hp, 200 psi, single-cylinder inverted-vertical barring engine.

The twin-tandem triple-expansion engine was popular for the high powers needed in the Lancashire spinning mills, and the Trencherfield engine is the last survivor of this layout. The two low-pressure cylinders are on each side of the engine nearest the crankshaft. Behind the left-hand LP cylinder is the HP cylinder and the intermediate pressure cylinder occupies a similar position on the right-hand side of the engine. The HP and IP inlet valves have trip gear, the HP being governor controlled and the IP hand adjusted. The LP inlet valves are driven by direct linkage

Trencherfield Mill. All the J. & E. Wood characteristics are present on this, the last surviving twin-tandem triple-expansion mill engine. Note the clean lines of the cylinders obtained by placing the valves underneath.

without trip gear. This arrangement is typical J. & E. Wood practice as is the placing of all the valves below the cylinders. The valve gear is operated by eccentrics and rods from the crankshaft and the flywheel is boarded to reduce windage. Electric drives replaced the engine in 1968, but cotton spinning ceased soon afterwards and the mill is now used as a warehouse.

Access is by prior application to the mill.

Trencherfield Mill. The largest surviving flywheel in the UK has grooves for fifty-four ropes. The carpentry work on the boarding is also most impressive.

TWYFORD PUMPING STATION, Winchester, Hampshire

INVERTED VERTICAL TRIPLE EXPANSION WATERWORKS PUMPING ENGINE
Hathorn, Davey & Co Ltd, Leeds, 1913, 17 in (HP), 27 in (IP), 46 in (LP) × 36 in stroke, Corliss valves, Craig's cam valve-gear, two well pumps, three force pumps, 25 rpm. Three Babcock & Wilcox water-tube boilers, 1916, hand fired, two wall-mounted inverted-vertical duplex feed-pumps.

Hathorn, Davey used Craig's cam gear both for Corliss and drop valves. The cams were of a special design which allowed easy control by variation of cut-off. They also receded quickly from the follower or valve stem at the point of cut-off thus minimising wear. On this engine the Corliss valves are fitted in the cylinder end covers. Three force pumps below the crankshaft delivered water to high-level storage and are coupled to the engine crossheads by side rods. To drive the well pumps a crank is fitted on an extension of the crankshaft beyond the flywheel, from which a timber connecting rod with flitch plates transmitted reciprocating motion to two bell cranks over the well. This equipment has now been removed to make room for the headgear of the four electric submersible pumps now installed. The water-tube boilers were ideal for efficient steam generation under steady load conditions. This was however the corrugated-iron age and the construction of the boiler house detracts from the typical waterworks engine house.

Access is by application to the Southern Water Authority, Hampshire Division, Southampton.

Twyford. A typical inverted vertical triple expansion waterworks pumping installation. Well pumps were driven from the end of the crankshaft and force pumps by side rods from the crossheads.

TURNFORD PUMPING STATION, Herts

SIDE-LEVER WATERWORKS PUMPING ENGINE
James Watt & Co, Soho Works, Birmingham, 1845, 28 in × 42 in, 15 rpm.

The side-lever engine was an adaptation of the beam engine to marine work. The whole engine was mounted upon a bedplate with all parts above it, including condenser and auxiliary pumps. The piston rod drove upwards to a 'T' head from which rods were taken down to the beams, low down on each side of the engine. The connecting rod was in the form of an inverted 'T' coupled to each beam by rods from the cross-piece. At sea the side-lever engine invariably drove paddle wheels. There were two forms of engine: one with the beams pivotted at the centre as at Turnford, while a second type had the beams pivotted at one end with the connecting rod taken from a point about one third the distance from the cylinder end. The Turnford engine was built for a low working pressure of about 10 psi. A second set of pumps was installed at the station in 1882 driven by a single-cylinder inverted-vertical engine by R. Moreland of London. Taking steam at 50-60 psi this engine exhausted to the side-lever engine.

Access is by application to the Thames Water Authority, Metropolitan Water Division, New River Head, London EC1.

TY-MAWR COLLIERY, Pontypridd, Glamorgan

TWIN CYLINDER HORIZONTAL COLLIERY WINDING ENGINE
Barclay & Cope, Kidsgrove, Staffs, 1875, 36 in × 72 in, piston valves.

At the present time this engine still works occasionally, although 'listed'. The motive power however is compressed air and not steam. It is cheaper to start up a compressor than fire a boiler for a short spell of work. One hopes that its listing as an ancient monument will continue to ensure its preservation. A noteworthy feature of the engine are the piston valves which may be original and are of exceptionally small diameter.

The engine is still in the ownership of the National Coal Board and is not accessible except by special arrangement.

WADWORTH & CO LTD, Northgate Brewery, Devizes, Wilts

SINGLE CYLINDER HORIZONTAL ENGINE
G. Adlam & Sons, Bristol, c 1885. 10 in × 18 in.

This relatively small engine ceased work in 1935, but has been kept in situ ever since. Application should be made to the brewery for viewing.

WEST HAM SEWAGE PUMPING STATION, London

WOOLF COMPOUND PUMPING ENGINES (2)
The Lilleshall Company, Oakengates, c 1895.

These are the last surviving beam engines of this maker.
There is some doubt about the future and the engines are not normally accessible.

APPENDIX

1   On Site Preservation.   Public Access on a Regular Basis
Additional Sites

COLDHARBOUR MILL, Uffculme, Devon
CROSS-COMPOUND HORIZONTAL MILL ENGINE
Pollit & Wigzell Ltd, Sowerby Bridge, 1910, 14½in (HP) × 27in (LP) × 42in stroke, piston drop valves (inlet), Corliss valves (exhaust), Whitehead governor, flywheel 13ft diameter grooved for 13-1½in diameter ropes. Jet condenser above floor behind LP cylinder. 90rpm, 120psi, 300hp. Single cylinder inverted vertical barring engine.

Wool spinning commenced at Coldharbour in 1799 by Thomas Fox and continued under Fox Brothers & Co Ltd, until 1981. The mill now operates as a working wool museum although the machinery is now electrically driven.

The mill is open seven days a week in summer and five days a week in winter. Full details from the mill. (Tel: 0884 40960)

ETRUSCAN BONE & STONE WORKS, Etruria, Stoke-on-Trent
SINGLE CYLINDER HOUSE-BUILT BEAM ENGINE
Attributed to Sherrat of Salford, about 1839, 30in × 60in, Watt-type governor, cruciform connecting rod, 22rpm, 85hp, 30psi, named *Princess.*

The whole works and engine are currently being restored and will be open to the public.

KIDWELLY TINPLATE WORKS MUSEUM, Kidwelly, Dyfed
Quite a new museum based on the former Kidwelly Tinplate Works. The rolling mill engines are still *in situ* and are of considerable interest. Additionally the winding engine and headgear from Morlais Colliery, Llangennech have been brought to the site and re-erected.

INVERTED VERTICAL TANDEM-COMPOUND HOT-ROLLING MILL ENGINE (2)
Edwin Foden, Sandbach, Cheshire, about 1880, rebuilt about 1892, 24in and 43in (approx) × 42in stroke, piston valves, condensing, 500hp, 26rpm.

The hot-roll is the first rolling stage in tinplate making, reducing the steel from short thick bars to thin and wide sheets. Enormous power was needed so that the number of passes through the rolls and the number of re-heats was kept to a minimum.

HORIZONTAL TANDEM-COMPOUND COLD-ROLLING MILL ENGINE
Cole, Marchent & Morley, Bradford, about 1920, piston drop valves, 500hp.

Cold rolling was the finishing process in the preparation of tinplate. Several passes are made through the rolls which planishes the sheets, but does not reduce the thickness.

HORIZONTAL TWIN-CYLINDER COLLIERY WINDING ENGINE
Andrew Barclay, Sons, & Co Ltd, Caledonia Works, Kilmarnock, 1907, 20in × 42in, Corliss valves (no trip gear), Stephenson valve gear.

LOCKE'S DISTILLERY, KILBEGGAN, Co Westmeath, Eire
CROSS - COMPOUND HORIZONTAL MILL ENGINE
Turnbull, Grant & Jack, Port Dundas, Glasgow, 1887. 14in (HP) × 22in (LP) × 36in stroke. Turnbull's patent cross cut-off slide valves (HP), plain slide valve (LP). Watt-type governor, flywheel 11ft diameter, jet condenser above floor behind LP cylinder, bevel gear drive to main shaft, 50rpm, 125hp (approx), 80psi.

Installed to supplement a 15ft diameter waterwheel the engine and wheel fell into disuse when the distillery closed in 1954. The Kilbeggan Development Association took over the buildings in 1983 and waterwheel and engine have been restored to working order by volunteers. Steam is now supplied by a modern package boiler. The distillery now houses a number of traditional craft trades and is open daily. The engine is steamed on several occasions during the summer.

SCOTTISH MINING MUSEUM, Lady Victoria Colliery, Newtongrange, Midlothian
TWIN CYLINDER HORIZONTAL WINDING ENGINE
Grant, Ritchie & Co, Kilmarnock, 1894, 42in × 84in. Cornish double-beat drop valves, Gooch valve gear, parallel winding drum 20ft diameter with caliper brakes. Gardner overwind/ Overspeed controller, winding depth 500yd, 100psi, non-condensing. Eight Lancashire boilers, hand fired, forced draught, 105psi.
A very large engine by any standards, Lady Victoria is the largest surviving winding engine in Scotland and second largest in the UK.
The colliery is open all year, daily except Monday.

STOTT PARK BOBBIN MILL, Newby Bridge, Cumbria
SINGLE CYLINDER HORIZONTAL MILL ENGINE
William Bradley, Brighouse, 1880, 12in × 24in, slide valve, Watt-type governor, disc crank, flywheel 7ft 8in diameter Cornish boiler by I. & B. Umpleby, 1880.

Stott Park Bobbin Mill formerly manufactured bobbins for the textile industry from locally grown timber. The machinery remains intact although now electrically driven and the mill is a museum under the auspices of the Department of the Environment.

Amendments to Existing Entries

Page 28 'THE ENGINE HOUSE', Nottingham.
Engine removed and re-erected at Nottingham Industrial Museum, Wollaton Park.

Page 28 GLENRUTHVEN MILL, Auchterarder.
Now in the ownership of Strathearn Developments Limited. Mill closed for textile production, but converted to a museum and exhibition centre. Access daily Easter-September. Engine in steam alternate week-ends mid-July to mid-September.

TOWER BRIDGE, London
TWIN-TANDEM COMPOUND HORIZONTAL HYDRAULIC POWER ENGINES (2)
Sir W. G. Armstrong, Mitchell & Co, Ltd, Gateshead, 1894. 18in (HP) × 30in (LP) × 36in stroke, slide valves, disc cranks, Porter governor, condenser (below floor), 28rpm (max), 360hp, 80psi, Lancashire boilers 85psi.

Before electricity became commonplace, water at high pressure — up to 1,000psi — was used to provide power. Cities had networks of high pressure water mains laid below the streets with branches into buildings, powering lifts and other machinery. Tower Bridge had its own system operating at 750psi, which was used until 1976.
Access to the bridge is daily and one of the engines is turned slowly using compressed air.

YORKSHIRE MINING MUSEUM, Caphouse Colliery, Middlestown, West Yorkshire
TWIN CYLINDER HORIZONTAL WINDING ENGINE
Davy Brothers, Sheffield, 1876, 16in × 36in, 9ft diameter drum, slide valves. Two Lancashire boilers, 80psi.

The highlight of this new colliery museum opened in 1988 is the visit to the underground workings. At the present time the engine has not been restored to working order.

Page 29-30 KEW BRIDGE PUMPING STATION, Brentford
Additional engine: cross-compound waterworks pumping engine, by James Simpson & Co, 1910, from Waddon Pumping Station.

Page 44-6 PRESTONGRANGE MINING MUSEUM, Prestonpans
Now part of the Scottish Mining Museum. Open all year, Tuesday-Sunday. Tel: 031 665 9904. Additional engine: inverted vertical high speed enclosed engine, direct coupled to a generator, by Browett, Lindley & Co Ltd.

2 Engines in Museums. Additional Museums

BRESSINGHAM STEAM MUSEUM, Diss, Norfolk
Founded in 1968 with the object of preserving railway locomotives, Bressingham has now acquired a significant collection of stationary steam engines,

A-FRAME SINGLE BEAM ENGINE FROM BANSTEAD HOSPITAL, SURREY
Easton & Anderson, 1870.

This engine was used to drive well-pumps supplying the hospital with water and was in service until 1980.

TWIN CYLINDER HORIZONTAL HYDRAULIC PUMPING ENGINE FROM CHIVER'S JAM FACTORY,
Histon, Cambridgeshire
Sir William Arrol & Co, Glasgow, 1902.

An example of the once extensive use of hydraulic power, this engine powered lifts in the factory.

Other exhibits include single cylinder horizontal engines by Vernon & Guest, Smethwick and Marshall of Gainsborough.

The museum is open every Sunday from the end of April to end of September, also Thursdays beginning of June to mid-September, Wednesdays in August plus the spring and summer Bank Holidays. (Tel: 037 988 382/386)

COTHEY BOTTOM HERITAGE CENTRE, Ryde, Isle of Wight
A recently opened museum forming part of the Westridge Leisure Centre complex.

SINGLE CYLINDER HORIZONTAL ENGINE FROM MOREY'S SHIPYARD, NEWPORT, IOW
Pollit & Wigzell Ltd, Sowerby Bridge, 1890, 13in × 24in, slide valve with Rider's semi-rotating automatic cut-off, weighted fly-ball governor, flywheel 6ft diameter.

SINGLE CYLINDER GRASSHOPPER BEAM ENGINE FROM MARVIN'S SHIPYARD, COWES
Easton, Amos & Sons, Southwark, about 1850, 10in × 20in, slide valve, single plate cast-iron beam, crank throw circle 14in diameter, flywheel 9ft diameter.

Supplied to Osborne House, the engine drove agricultural machinery, the sawmill, and pumped water for the fountains. It was sold to the shipyard in 1904 where it was used until 1962 to power a slipway winch.

GREATER MANCHESTER MUSEUM OF SCIENCE & INDUSTRY, Lower Byrom Street, Liverpool Road, Manchester
Formerly housed in cramped premises the museum is now established on the Liverpool Road Station site of the former Liverpool & Manchester Railway. It must rank as one of the leading technological museums in the world. Many stationary steam engines are exhibited and these are regularly run under steam.

SINGLE CYLINDER HOUSE-BUILT BEAM ENGINE FROM HAYDOCK COLLIERIES
Maker unknown, about 1825, 25in × 60in, slide valves, Watt-type governor, toothed flywheel 15ft diameter, single-plate cast-iron beam, 20rpm approx, 8psi.

This engine was erected second-hand in 1863 to drive the joinery shop of Richard Evans's Haydock Collieries. It represents early steam engine practice where most of the power was derived from condenser vacuum.

SINGLE CYLINDER HORIZONTAL MILL ENGINE FROM DURN MILL, LITTLE-BOROUGH
Earnshaw & Holt, Rochdale, 1864, 28in × 48in, slide valve, Porter-type governor on throttle valve, flywheel 15ft diameter, gear drive to mill, 63rpm, 250hp, 60psi.

TANDEM COMPOUND HORIZONTAL MILL ENGINE FROM FIRGROVE MILL, ROCHDALE
J. & W. McNaught, Rochdale, 1907, 15in (HP) × 31in (LP) × 48in stroke, Corliss valves (HP), expansion slide valves (LP), Lumb's governor, flywheel 15ft diameter, ten ropes, jet condenser (below floor), 500hp, 80rpm, 180psi.

A classic example of the medium-power mill engines of the period which were to be found in cotton mills all over Lancashire.

CROSS-COMPOUND HORIZONTAL EXTRACTION UNIFLOW ENGINE FROM ELM STREET MILL, BURNLEY
W. & J. Galloway Ltd, Manchester, 1926, 21in (HP) × 37in (LP) × 36in stroke, drop inlet valves with Pilling's patent oil-hydraulic valve gear, piston drop exhaust valves (HP only), Uniflow LP cylinder, flywheel 11ft 6in dia-

meter, sixteen ropes, balanced cranks, forced lubrication, 125rpm, 800hp, 150psi.

This engine is now unique in the U.K. representing the final development of the mill engine and the principle of steam extraction for process between the high-pressure and low-pressure cylinders.

INVERTED VERTICAL CROSS-COMPOUND ENCLOSED GENERATING ENGINE
S.Z. de Ferranti Ltd., 1900, No 381

Originally built for Lambeth Power Station and fitted with a flywheel alternator this engine was sold to Brunswick Mill in 1920 where it was fitted with a flywheel for driving the mill by ropes. In 1952 it was removed for preservation by Basil de Ferranti and has now been transferred to the museum.

HOME FARM, TATTON PARK, Knutsford, Cheshire (National Trust)
SINGLE CYLINDER HORIZONTAL ENGINE
Maker unknown, possibly Mark Shaw & Sons, Milnsbridge, about 1890, 12¾in × 25½in, slide valve, Pickering governor, flywheel 6ft 9in diameter.

This engine replaces a long scrapped engine at the same location. It was removed by an enthusiast from the works of the Colne Vale Dye & Chemical Co, Milnsbridge, Huddersfield in 1981 who later donated it to the National Trust. The engine is in working order and can be run under steam.

LAUNCESTON STEAM RAILWAY,
St Thomas Road, Launceston, Cornwall
The museum associated with this railway contains several stationary and other engines restored by the Robey Trust. The stationary steam engines at present operate on compressed air. Access is at Easter weekend, then Sundays to the Spring Bank Holiday. Open daily Spring Bank Holiday to end of September and at week-ends until end of October. (Tel: Launceston 5665)

SINGLE-CYLINDER HORIZONTAL DROP-VALVE ENGINE
FROM FAIRFIELD HOSPITAL, HITCHIN

Robey & Co Ltd, Lincoln 1904, No 24462, 11¾in × 24in, drop valves with Robey's patent trip gear, girder or 'bayonet' bed, flywheel 8ft diameter, 63hp, 120rpm.

The engine was installed to drive laundry machinery and two sets of pumps for water supply.

SINGLE-CYLINDER HORIZONTAL LABORATORY ENGINE
Robey & Co Ltd, Lincoln, 1935, No 52309, 5¾in × 8in, Meyer expansion slide valve, flywheel 3ft 6in diameter.

Built for the purpose of experiments in applied thermodynamics in the heat engines laboratory at Oxford University this engine is complete with Crosby indicators and tachograph.

TWIN-CYLINDER HORIZONTAL WINDING ENGINE
FROM PENRHIWCEIBER COLLIERY, SOUTH WALES
Robey & Co Ltd, Lincoln 1911, Nos 30082 (left-hand engine) and 30083 (right-hand engine), 18 × 33in, drop valves with Robey's patent trip gear and steam reversing gear.

Made for the Penrikyber Navigation & Colliery Co, the engine was in service until 1978. Although Robey & Co's works were well removed from any colliery, they nevertheless made many winding engines

LEEDS INDUSTRIAL MUSEUM, Armley Mills, Canal Road, Leeds
Quite a recent addition to the growing total of industrial museums, Armley Mills has much of steam interest, including two interesting stationary engines.

SINGLE-CYLINDER UNIFLOW HORIZONTAL MILL ENGINE
FROM DOBROYD LTD, NEW MILLS, HOLMFIRTH
Pollit & Wigzell Ltd, Sowerby Bridge, 1924, 24in × 30in, piston drop valves, Whitehead governor, 132rpm, 500hp, 160psi.

Pollit & Wigzell made their first venture in Uniflow engine design with this engine and to give it a good trial used it to drive their own works. No doubt it was also used for marketing purposes for potential customers.

TANDEM COMPOUND HORIZONTAL MILL ENGINE FROM PROVIDENCE DYE WORKS, WORTLEY

Woodhouse & Mitchell, Brighouse, about 1890, 10¾in (HP) × 18in (LP) × 36in stroke, Corliss valves (HP), slide valve (LP), cross-arm governor, 100hp, 80rpm, 80psi.

Some stationary engines were surprisingly mobile and the original location of this engine is unknown. By 1910 it was driving a flour mill in Maidstone and in 1925 moved again to the Providence Dye Works where it worked until about 1965.

MUSEUM OF LINCOLNSHIRE LIFE,
Burton Road, Lincoln

The museum has a small collection of engines built in the City of Lincoln by Robey & Co, Ruston, Proctor & Co Ltd., and Ruston & Hornsby Ltd. The types range from high speed inverted-vertical to conventional horizontal engines. The oldest in the collection is a Robey horizontal engine of 1880. In addition to the stationary steam engines there is a small but interesting collection of oil and gas engines which were built locally.

PENRITH STEAM MUSEUM. Castle-gate Foundry, Penrith, Cumbria

This is a new and privately owned museum with an extensive collection of road engines as well as two interesting stationary steam engines. The standard of restoration is very high. Access is Sunday to Friday, Easter — end September.

TANDEM COMPOUND HORIZONTAL MILL ENGINE FROM KRUMLIN MILL, BARK-ISLAND, YORKS

Pollit & Wigzell, Sowerby Bridge, 1899, 11½in (HP) × 23in (LP) × 36in stroke, Corliss valves (HP), slide valve (LP), Lumb's governor, flywheel 12ft diameter, seven ropes, jet condenser (above floor), 85rpm, 180ihp, 150psi, named *Judith Hannah*.

To reduce the overall length of tandem compound engines, Pollit & Wigzell introduced their patent three-piston rod engine. The high-pressure/low-pressure cylinders abutted and the low pressure piston had two piston rods

which straddled the high-pressure cylinder. *Judith Hannah* was one of two engines supplied to the London General Omnibus Co, for straw cutting when London buses were horse drawn. The engine went to Krumlin Mill in 1919 replacing an 1864 beam engine. At the museum the engine is demonstrated in motion using an electric motor.

SINGLE CYLINDER UNDERTYPE SEMI-PORTABLE ENGINE

Robey & Co, Lincoln, about 1935, works number 49166, 8in × 12in, slide valve, Pickering governor, 5 nominal hp, 140rpm, locomotive-type boiler, 80psi.

Most of the traction engine builders in the UK made a range of semi-portable engines in which the engine and boiler were mounted on one strong bed. The cylinders could be mounted on top of the firebox (overtype) or under the smokebox (undertype), the latter having a resemblance to railway locomotives. Only two undertype semi-portable engines are known to survive in the UK.

SHEFFIELD INDUSTRIAL MUSEUM,
Kelham Island, Sheffield

THREE-CYLINDER INVERTED-VERTICAL REVERSING ROLLING MILL ENGINE FROM RIVER DON WORKS

Davy Brothers, Sheffield, 1905, 40in × 48in, piston valves, Joy's valve gear, 120rpm maximum, 12,000hp, 160psi.

This is the most powerful steam engine surviving in the UK. It was originally supplied to Cammell's Grimesthorpe Works where it produced thousands of tons of steel armour plate for the Royal Navy, including 16in-thick plate for *King George V* class battleships.

Speed is essential in rolling steel plates and the reversing gear is hydraulically operated. The engine would slow down, stop, reverse and accelerate to full speed again in the space of two seconds!

The engine is demonstrated without load on a daily basis at the museum.

STRUMPSHAW OLD HALL MUSEUM,
STRUMPSHAW, near NORWICH

This now extensive museum houses a collection of various stationary engines, traction engines and agricultural machinery. Much of the collection is of eastern England manufacture and illustrates well the diversity of products made in this region. Many of the engines are demonstrated running, using compressed air instead of steam.

SINGLE-CYLINDER HORIZONTAL DROP-VALVE ENGINE FROM TIPTREE JAM FACTORY, MISTLEY

Marshall & Sons, Gainsborough, 1927

A classic late design of Marshall engine. The use of drop valves with governor-controlled cut-off, in this case a Proell governor, gave maximum possible economy.

A-FRAME WOOLF COMPOUND WATERWORKS PUMPING ENGINE FROM ADDINGTON PUMPING STATION, CROYDON

Glenfield & Co Ltd, Kilmarnock, 1893, 20in × 48in (HP), 34in × 72in (LP), slide valves, Porter governor, flywheel 18ft diameter, 18rpm.

With its older sister made by Easton & Anderson in 1888, this was the last waterworks beam pumping engine in service, continuing at work until 1975.

Other engines being made ready for display at the museum are a Worthington-Simpson cross-compound waterworks pumping engine of 1915 and a superb little Robey 'Uniflow' engine.

The museum is open mid-May to the end of September in the afternoons, Sunday to Friday.

SUMMERLEE HERITAGE MUSEUM,
Coatbridge, Strathclyde
TWIN-CYLINDER HORIZONTAL WINDING ENGINE FROM CARDOWAN COLLIERY, STEPPS

Murray & Patterson, Coatbridge, 1924, 26in × 60in, piston valves, Stephenson's link valve gear, parallel winding drum 13ft diameter, winding depth 340 fathoms (2,040ft) 170psi.

One of two sets of identical winding engines built for the then new Cardowan Colliery. Both engines served throughout the life of the colliery to 1984.

Amendments to Existing Entries

Page 52-6 BIRMINGHAM MUSEUM OF SCIENCE AND INDUSTRY

Additional engine: Boulton & Watt pumping engine of 1779, from Ocker Hill, 33in × 96in. Workable under steam.

Note that other Pollit & Wigzell engines are now on public display in museums.

Page 56 BLACK COUNTRY MUSEUM, Dudley.

Additional engine: Working replica of the first Newcomen engine erected at Dudley in 1712.

Page 61-3 FORNCETT INDUSTRIAL STEAM ENGINE, Norwich.

Additional engines: Hick, Hargreaves single-cylinder horizontal Corliss valve engine.
Woolf compound A-frame beam pumping engine by Easton & Anderson, from Roall Pumping Station.
Marshall single-cylinder horizontal engine.
Single-cylinder house-built beam pumping engine, Gimson & Co, 1879, from Hopwas Pumping Station (not yet erected).

Page 64 INDUSTRIAL & SOCIAL HISTORY MUSEUM, Kirkcaldy

The Douglas & Grant engine has now been erected in the Royal Scottish Museum store, Newbattle, which is open occasionally.

Page 70 NEWCASTLE-UPON-TYNE MUSEUM OF SCIENCE & ENGINEERING

Now transferred to West Blandford Street, Newcastle-upon-Tyne.

Page 74 NORTH WESTERN MUSEUM OF SCIENCE & INDUSTRY

Now transferred to Liverpool Road Station, Manchester as The Greater Manchester Museum of Science & Industry

3 On Site Preservation. Access on Open Days

Additional Sites

HERITAGE BREWERY, Anglesey Road, Burton-on-Trent, Staffs
SINGLE-CYLINDER HORIZONTAL ENGINE
Buxton & Thornley, Burton-on-Trent, 1881, 9in × 18in, expansion slide valve, Pickering governor, 'bent' crank, flywheel 7ft diameter, belt pulley 3ft 6in diameter.

Buxton & Thornley were brewery engineers who supplied complete plant for the brewing of beer, including the steam engines to drive it.
    The brewery is open for visits by organised parties and in addition there are open days from time to time. Details from the brewery. Tel: Burton-on-Trent 69226.

SKOPOS FABRICS, Providence Mills, Earlsheaton, Dewsbury, West Yorks
TANDEM COMPOUND HORIZONTAL MILL ENGINE
W. & J. Cardwell; Dewsbury, 1883 (as single-cylinder engine), rebuilt Woodhouse & Mitchell, Brighouse, 1894, 15in (HP) × 21in (LP) × 42in stroke (approx), Corliss valves (HP), slide valve (LP), Proell governor, 80rpm, 300hp, 120psi.

The engine was rebuilt in its present form when the mill was rebuilt following a fire in 1894. Although suffering a fractured bedplate during its career the engine ran until 1965. Restoration was completed in 1986.

Amendments to Existing Entries

Page 95 **BANCROFT SHED,** Barnoldswick
The cylinder sizes are 17in (HP) × 34in (LP) × 48in stroke.

Page 98 **CHEDDARS LANE,** Cambridge
One engine is now steamable.

Page 100 **DEE MILL,** Shaw
The mill has been closed and demolished. Engine retained but at present not accessible.

Page 102 **DIAMOND WORKS,** Royton
Access is now by application to the works. There are now no regular open days.

Page 105 **MILL MEECE PUMPING STATION,** Eccleshall
Access now Sunday afternoons April-September. Engines in steam third weekend of each month.

4 On Site Preservation. Access by Arrangement Only

Additional Site

WESTWOOD YARNS LTD, Washpit Mills, Holmfirth, West Yorks
TANDEM COMPOUND HORIZONTAL MILL ENGINE
Pollit & Wigzell Ltd, Sowerby Bridge, 1909, 18in (HP) × 34in (LP) × 48in stroke, Corliss valves, Lumb's governor, flywheel 21ft diameter, eighteen ropes, 82rpm, 610hp, 150psi, named *Agnes*.

A magnificent example of the maker's patent three-piston rod tandem compound engine which is maintained in immaculate condition by an enthusiastic engineer. Access is by prior arrangement on Friday afternoons.

Amendments to Existing Entries

Page 107 **ABERGORKI COLLIERY,** Mountain Ash
Engine removed to store at Big Pit Museum, Blaenavon.

Page 108 **APPLETON,** Sandringham
Engine removed to store at Ironbridge.

Page 108 **BAITING MILL,** Rochdale
Mill now closed, future uncertain.

Page 109 **BEELEIGH MILL,** Maldon
Owners now Essex Water Company, Romford.

Page 111 **BRAYTON PUMPING STA-TION,** Selby
Engine now removed for private preservation.

Page 111-12 **BRINDLEY BANK,** Rugeley
Page 136 `MAPLE BROOK,` Lichfield
Change of address, now: South Staffordshire Water Company, Green Lane, Walsall.

Page 112 **BRITISH LEYLAND,** Chorley
Engine now removed to store by Chorley District Council.

Page 113 **BROKEN SCAR,** Darlington
Engine now in care of a trust. Access is on open days and engine is run under steam.

Page 120 **CROSS LANE MILL,** Skipton
Mill closed for textile production and under new ownership. Access by application to Fray Design Marketing Ltd at the mill.

Page 122 **DALMORE DISTILLERY,** Alnes
Now closed.

Page 123 **DOVER PUMPING STATION**
Now Dover Museum of Transport

Page 123 **ELDER & WATSON,** Strathaven
Works demolished. Engine in store at New Lanark.

Page 123 **ELLESMERE PORT**
Now open daily. Engines in steam from time to time.

Page 124 **ELLENROAD RING MILL**
Mill demolished. Engine and house retained. Scheduled to be open to the public. Details from S. Graham, Ellenroad Trust, 41 Bark Lane, Ilkley, West Yorks.

Page 125 **FELSTOR LTD,** Raunds
Works now closed.

Page 125 **FENLAND LAUNDRIES,** Grantham
Engine now removed for private preservation.

Page 126 **FERRANTI LTD,** Hollingwood
Engine now installed at Greater Manchester Museum of Science & Industry

Page 127 **FLEAM DYKE,** Cambridge
Engines now scrapped

Page 128 **GALE'S BREWERY**
Engines now removed for private preservation.

Page 130 **HOPWAS PUMPING STA-TION**
Engines now removed. One to Forncett Industrial Museum, one to Leicestershire County Council store.

Page 131 **LEIGH SPINNERS,** Leigh
Access now by application to the firm at Butt's Bridge Mill, Park Lane, Leigh.

Page 135 **LUMBHOLE MILL,** Kettleshulme
Access now by application to the owner A. J. Sheldon.

Page 139 **PRINCES DRIVE,** Leamington Spa.
The pumping station is now demolished. The engines have been removed to store pending preservation elsewhere by other bodies.

Page 140 **ROALL PUMPING STATION,** Eggborough
Engine removed to Forncett Industrial Steam Museum.

Page 147 **TRENCHERFIELD MILL**
Now open daily all year. Engine in steam Saturday to Wednesday.
Additional engines:
Cross compound horizontal fan engine, Walker Bros, Wigan, 1912, from Sutton Manor Colliery.
Single cylinder horizontal drop valve engine and gas compressor, Walker Bros, Wigan, from ICI Mond Division, Northwich.

Page 147 **STOTHERT & PITT,** Bath
Engine now at Bath University.

Page 149 **TY-MAWR COLLIERY,** Pontypridd
Correction: *Barker* & Cope. Engine now owned by local authority. Not accessible at the present time.

INDEX

Index of places and original engine locations.
References to the Appendix are in **bold** and should be consulted first.
PS = Pumping Station

Abbey PS, see Leicestershire Museum of Technology
Abbots Hall Museum, 50
Aberbeeg Colliery, see Welsh Industrial and Maritime Museum
Abergorki Colliery, 107, **156**
Addington PS, **155**
Albert Hall, see Newcastle upon Tyne Museum of Science & Engineering
Aller Moor PS, 107
All Saints Brewery, 15
Alma Tannery, see Bankfield Museum
Appleton PS, 108, **156**
Astley Green Colliery, 96
Aston Expressway, 50
Atlas Mill, see Northern Mill Engines Society
Atkinson's Chemical Works, see Science Museum

Bagg's Brewery, see Bridewell Museum
Baiting Mill, 108-9, **156**
Bamford Mill, see Carbolite Furnaces Ltd
Bancroft Shed, 95, **156**
Bankfield Museum, 50
Banstead Hospital, **152**
Barclay & Perkins Brewery, see Royal Scottish Museum
Barry UDC, see Welsh Industrial and Maritime Museum
Basford PS, see Nottingham Industrial Museum
Bass Museum, 50-1
Beamish Colliery, see North of England Open Air Museum
Beechwood Brushes, see Hollycombe House
Beeleigh Mill, 109, **156**
Belfast Sewage Works, see No 1 PS
Bestwood Colliery, 109
Biggar Gasworks, 51
Birmingham Museum of Science & Industry, 52-6, **155**
Black Country Museum, 56, **155**
Blaenant Colliery, see Cefn Coed Coal & Steam Centre
Blagdon PS, 110
Bland's Timberyard, see Welsh Industrial & Maritime Museum

Bolton, 58
Bradford Industrial Museum, 58
Brayton PS, 111, **157**
Brede PS, 111
Brereton Mill, 111
Bressingham Steam Museum, **151**
Bridewell Museum, 59
Brighton & Hove Engineerium, 17-19
Brighton Mental Hospital, see Royal Scottish Museum
Brimrod Steam Laundry, see Newcastle upon Tyne Museum of Science & Engineering
Brindley Bank PS, 111-12, **157**
Bristol Waterworks Co, see: Blagdon PS and Chelvey PS
British Leyland, 112, **157**
British Rail, see Shore Road PS
Broken Scar Waterworks, 113, **157**
Bromsberrow PS, 114
Broomfleet Brickworks, see Newcastle upon Tyne Museum of Science & Engineering
Broomy Hill Waterworks, 19-20
Brunswick Mill, **153**
Bygones Museum, 58

Cadoxton Brewery, see Welsh Industrial & Maritime Museum
Cambridge Water Co, see Fleam Dyke PS
Carbolite Furnaces Ltd, 97
Cardiff Waterworks, see Welsh Industrial & Maritime Museum
Cardowan Colliery, **155**
Cefn Coed Coal & Steam Centre, 15-16
Chamber & Fargus, see Science Museum
Chatterley-Whitfield Colliery Museum, 20-1
Chauntry Mill, see D. Gurteen & Sons Ltd
Cheddar's Lane Sewage Works, 98, **156**
Cheddleton Flint Mill, 59
Chelvey PS, 114
Cherry Garden S, 115-116
Chiver's Jam Factory, **152**
Clay Mills Sewage Works, 118-19
Clark, C. & J., 117
Cliftonville Waterworks, see Kew Bridge Pumping Station
Coldharbour Mill, **150**
Coleham PS, 22
Combe Sawmill, 99
Cothy Bottom Heritage Centre, **152**

Cottingham PS, 120
Coventry Canal, see Dartmouth
Crofton PS, 23-4
Cromford Canal, see Lea Wood
Cromford & High Peak Railway, see Middleton Incline
Crossfield Mill, see Northern Mill Engines Society Museum
Cross Lane Mill, 120
Crossness Sewage Works, 120
Croydon Gasworks, see Wendron Forge
Crumlin Navigation Colliery, see Welsh Industrial & Maritime Museum
Curry Moor PS, 121

Dalmore Distillery, 122, **157**
Dancer's End PS, see Kew Bridge PS
Dartmouth, 59
Darwen, 60
Dee Mill, 100-1, **156**
Denge PS, 122. See also Cherry Garden PS
Devenish Weymouth Brewery, 122
Devon Colliery, 16
Diamond Works, 102
Dobroyd Ltd, **153**
Dogdyke PS, 103
Donisthorpe Colliery, see National Mining Museum
Dover PS, 123, **157**
Dover Museum of Transport, **157**
Drapersfield, see Ulster Museum
Dunoon Gasworks, see Biggar Gasworks
Dunston Gasworks, see Newcastle upon Tyne Museum of Science & Engineering
Durn Mill, **152**

East Anglian Water Company, see Lound PS
Eastney PS, 25
East Pool Mine, 25-7
Elba Steel Works, see Wendron Forge
Elder & Watson, 123, **157**
Ellen Road Ring Mill, 124, **157**
Ellesmere Port Canal Docks, 123, **157**
Elliot Colliery East Pit, 125
Ellistown Colliery, see National Mining Museum
Elm street Mill, **152**
Elsecar Colliery, 125
'The Engine House', 28, **151**
Englefield Estate Sawmill, 103

English China Clays Ltd, see Parkandillick Clayworks
Erddig Estate, 28
Essex Water Co, see Langford PS
Etruscan Bone Mill, 125, **150**

Fairfield Hospital, **153**
Falls Flax Spinning Co, see Ulster Museum
Felstor Ltd, 125, **157**
Fenland Laundries Ltd, 125, **157**
Ferranti Ltd, 126, **157**
Fettykill Mills, 127
Firgrove Mill, **152**
Fleam Dyke PS, 127-8, **157**
Folkestone & District Water Co, see: Cherry Garden PS, Denge PS and Dover PS, Forncett Industrial Museum
Forncett Industrial Museum, 61-3, **155**
Forth Bank Power Station, see Newcastle upon Tyne Museum of Science & Engineering

Gale's Brewery, 128, **157**
Garlogie Tweed Mill, 128
Gateshead Technical College, see Newcastle upon Tyne Museum of Science & Engineering
Geevor Tin Mines Ltd, see Levant Mine
Gladstone Pottery Museum, 75
Glamorgan Colliery, see Welsh Industrial & Maritime Museum
Glemsford Silk Mill, see Newcastle upon Tyne Museum of Science & Engineering
Glenruthven Mill, 28, **151**
Glentana Mills, see Industrial & Social History Museum Kirkcaldy
Glyn Pits, 129
'Golden Lion', 128
Goldstone PS, see Brighton & Hove Engineerium
Grazebrook, M. & W., Ltd, see Aston Expressway
Greater Manchester Museum of Science & Technology, **152-3**
Greensplat Clayworks, see Wendron Forge
Gurteen, D., & Sons Ltd, 104
Gus, Lee & Boswell, see Forncett Industrial Museum

Hall and Woodhouse Brewery, 128
Hamilton Museum, 65
Harrison & Mayer, see Gladstone Pottery Museum
Hatfield Main Colliery, see Welsh Industrial & Maritime Museum

Hawkesbury Junction, see Dartmouth
Haydock Collieries, **152**
Hearl, Heaton & Co, see Bradford Industrial Museum
Heath House Mill, see Wortley Top Forge
Helston Workhouse, see Wendron Forge
Henwood PS, 129
Heritage Brewery, **156**
Higher Mill Museum, Helmshore, 65
Hollycombe House, 66
Holroyd, J. & Co, 66
Hopwas PS, 130, **157**

ICI, see Wendron Forge
India Mill, see Darwen
Industrial & Social History Museum, Kirkcaldy, 64, **155**
Ironbridge Gorge Museum, 56-7

Kennett & Avon Canal, see Crofton PS
Kew Bridge PuS, 29-34, **151**
Kew Gardens, see Science Museum
Kidwelly Tinplate Works, **150**
King & Barnes Brewery, 131
Knowles, J. & Sons, see Staffordshire County Museum
Krumlin Mill, **154**

Lambeth PS, **153**
Langford PS, 131
Launceston Steam Railway, **153**
Lea Wood PS, 35-6
Leeds Industrial Museum, **153**
Leicestershire Museum of Technology, 37-9
Leigh Spinners Ltd, 131, **157**
Levant Mine, 132-3
Lincolnshire Life, Museum of, **154**
Littleton PS, 133
Llanharry Iron Ore Mine, see Welsh Industrial & Maritime Museum
Llantwit Major Sawmill, see Welsh Industrial & Maritime Museum
Locke's Distillery, **150**
Longlands Farm, 134
Loughborough University, 66
Lound PS, 134
Low Hall Farm Sewage Works, 134
Low Bentham Silk Mill, see Bolton
Lower Standen Waterworks, see Cherry Garden PS
Lumbhole Mill, 135, **157**

Lyon's Corner House, see Forncett Industrial Museum

Maple Brook PS, 136, **157**
Margate Brewery, see Royal Scottish Museum
Markfield Road PS, 40
Marvin's Shipyard, **152**
Mathews, E. & A., see Bradford Industrial Museum
Metropolitan Water Board, see: Loughborough University; Science Museum
Middleton Incline, 41
Mid-Kent Water Co, see Henwood PuS
Millmeece PS, 105, **156**

Minton's Pottery Works, see Cheddleton Flint Mill
Monk's Hall Museum, 67
Monmouth Gasworks, see Welsh Industrial Museum
Morey's Shipyard, **152**
Morlais Colliery, **150**

National Coal Board, see: Elsecar Colliery; Ty-Mawr Colliery
National Mining Museum, 68
National Railway Museum, 69
Neepsend Gasworks, see Wortley Top Forge
Newcastle upon Tyne Museum of Science & Engineering, 70-1
Newcraighall Colliery, see Prestongrange Colliery Museum
Newport Tube Works, see Welsh Industrial & Maritime Museum
Newton Abbot Power Station, see Wendron Forge
Nixon's Navigation Colliery, see Welsh Industrial and Maritime Museum
Northern Mill Engines Society Museum, 72-4
North of England Open Air Museum, 71-2
Northumbrian Water Authority, see Broken Scar Waterworks
North Western Museum of Science and Industry, 74, **155**
Norwich Gas Works, see Thursford Collection
Nottingham Industrial Museum, 76
No 1 PS, Belfast, 136

Oak Lee Mills, see Bradford Industrial Museum
Ormskirk Poor Law Institute, see Newcastle upon Tyne Museum of Science and Engineering
Owston Ferry PS 137

Oxford University, 153

Paddington Technical College, see Wendron Forge
Papplewick PS, 42
Park Colliery, see Welsh Industrial Museum
Parkandillick Clayworks, 138
Parkgate Iron & Steel Works, see Wortley Top Forge
Park Street Shed, see Northern Mill Engines Society Museum
Pearsall's Silk Mill, see Somerset County Museum
Pentrich Colliery, see Science Museum
Penrhiwceiber Colliery, 153
Penrith Steam Museum, 154
Pinchbeck PS, 40
Pinkney's Green Brickworks, see Wendron Forge
Pinsley View Mill, see Science Museum
Plessey Mill, see Newcastle upon Tyne Museum of Science & Engineering
Poole, 76
Poplar Gasworks, see Forncett Industrial Museum
Port of Bristol Authority, 139
Portsmouth Waterworks Company, see Eastney PS
Prestongrange Mining Museum, 44-6, 151
Princes Drive Sewage PS, 139, 157
Princes Warfe, Bristol, 139
Providence Dye Works, 154
Ram Brewery, 139
Redfern, Thomas, see Higher Mill Museum
Reeds Paper Mills, see Forncett Industrial Museum
River Don Works, 154
Roall PS, 140
Rotherham Technical College, see Wortley Top Forge
Royal Navy, see Wortley Top Forge
Royal Scottish Museum, 76-9
Runtlings Mill, 141
Ryhope PS, 46-7

Sanderson, Kayser Ltd, see Wortley Top Forge
Sandfields PS, 142
Sarston's Vinegar Works, see Forncett Industrial Museum
Science Museum, 79-83
Scottish Mining Museum, 151
Severn-Trent Water Authority, see: Bromsberrow PS; Clay Mills Sewage Works;

Millmeece PS; Princes Drive Sewage Works
Shearway PS, see Cherry Garden PS
Sheffield Industrial Museum, 154
Shirebrook Colliery, see National Mining Museum
Shore Road PS, 143
Sleaford Maltings, see: Bass Museum; Forncett Industrial Museum
Skopos Fabrics, 156
Skona Brewery, see Hall & Woodhouse Brewery
Soho Works, see Science Museum
Solway Flour Mills, 143
Somerset County Museum, 83
South Axholme Drainage Board, see Owston Ferry PS
South Crofty Mine, 144; see also Wendron Forge
Southern Water Authority, see: Brede PS; Twyford PS
Southfields PS, see Kew Bridge PS
South Staffordshire Waterworks Company, see: Brindley Bank PS; Hopwas PS; Maple Brook PS; Sandfields PS
Springfield Hospital, see Science Museum
Springhead PS, 145
Staffordshire County Museum, 83
St Ann's Brewery, see Royal Scottish Museum
St Leonard's Brewery, see Royal Scottish Museum
St Mary's Mill, 146
Stothert & Pitt Ltd, 147, 157
Stott Park Bobbin Mill, 151
Stretham PS, 48-9
Strumpshaw Old Hall Museum, 154
Summerlee Heritage Museum, 155
Sunderland Technical College, see Newcastle upon Tyne Museum of Science & Engineering
Sunnybank Mill, see Darwen
Swannington Incline, see National Railway Museum
Sydenham Sawmill, see Poole

Tees Cottage Works, see Broken Scar Waterworks
Tennants Brewery, see Newcastle upon Tyne Museum of Science & Engineering
Thames Water Authority, see: Crossness Sewage Works; Littleton PS; Turnford PS
Thursford Collection, 84
Tiptree Jam Factory, 155
Tollemach & Cobbold Breweries,

Ltd, 147
Tolson Memorial Museum, 83
Tower Bridge, 151, see also Forncett Industrial Museum
Trencherfield Mill, 147-8, 157
Turnford PS, 149
Twyford PS, 148
Ty-Mawr Colliery, 149, 157
Tyne Swing Bridge, see Newcastle upon Tyne Museum of Science & Engineering

Ulster Museum, 84
Ulster Woollen Mills, see Ulster Museum
Underfall Yard Workshops, see Port of Bristol Authority
University of Wales, see Welsh Industrial & Maritime Museum

Waddon PS, 151
Wadworth & Cc Ltd, 149
Washington 'F' Pit, 49
Wasp Mill, see Northern Mill Engines Society Museum
Weatherhill Incline, see National Railway Museum
Welsh Industrial & Maritime Museum, 85-9
Wendron Forge, 90-3
West Ham Sewage PS, 149
Westminster Hospital, see Forncett Industrial Museum
Westonzoyland PS, 106
Westwood Yarns, 156
White, John & Sons, Tannery, see Bradford Industrial Museum
Whitelees Mill, see J. Holroyd
Winchester Refuse Destructor, see Wendron Forge
Woodhorn Colliery, see Newcastle upon Tyne Museum of Science & Industry
Wortley Top Forge, 93-4

York City Asylum, see Newcastle upon Tyne Museum of Science & Engineering
Yorkshire Mining Museum, 151
Yorkshire Water Authority, see: Brayton PS; Cottingham PS; Roall PS; Springhead PS

160